NORSE MYTHOLOGY ...

ACCORDING TO UNCLE EINAR

To the Brainerd Memorial Library — Jane T. Sibley

NORSE MYTHOLOGY ...

ACCORDING TO UNCLE EINAR

JANE T. SIBLEY

ILLUSTRATIONS BY JOEL A. LEIB

COPYRIGHT © 2000 BY JANE T. SIBLEY.

LIBRARY OF CONGRESS NUMBER: 00-192529

ISBN #: HARDCOVER 0-7388-4418-7

SOFTCOVER 0-7388-4419-5

This is a work of fiction. Names, characters, places and incidents either are the product of the author's imagination or are used fictitiously, and any resemblance to any actual persons, living or dead, events, or locales is entirely coincidental.

This book was printed in the United States of America.

To order additional copies of this book, contact:

Xlibris Corporation

1-888-7-XLIBRIS

www.Xlibris.com

Orders@Xlibris.com

CONTENTS

How Asgard was Built, and How Odin Got a Horse 9

How Tyr Got his Purple Heart 18

The Big Heist 27

Freyja's Little Secret 39

How Thor Lost his Hammer and Freyja Didn't Get Hitched 49

The Day it Rained Mead 57

Thor's Summer Vacation (Part One) 63

Thor's Summer Vacation, (Part Two) 76

Thor's Fishing Trip 95

The Counterfeit Suitor 105

Showdown at the Jotunheim Corral 116

Thor and the Masked Madwomen 133

The Dating Game 145

How Balder Bought The Farm 161

Loki Lips Off 169

Loki's Terrible Day 178

The War to End All 189

The Lay of the Land 197

Dramatis Personae 201

Jane: To my wonderful parents, J. Ross & Edith M. Sibley, who had the courage to live on a small boat with 3 children for 5 glorious summers in Scandinavia.

Joel: For my family - all of them.

Chapter 1

How Asgard was Built, and How Odin Got a Horse

All right, children, Uncle Einar is going to tell you about the old days, when the gods walked the earth and the Vikings were busy "shopping" for trinkets down south in Britain and France. The old gods were just ordinary folks like us, except they could use magic and they didn't go to church. After all, they *were* gods and goddesses themselves. I suppose they could pray to each other, but somehow I don't think they did. They mostly lived like us, only more so.

Once upon a time, back when Asgard was still a backwater hamlet, a bunch of folks called the Æsir decided to move in. For one thing, the mill rate was low, crime was almost non-existent, and it was an easy commute to work. Real estate prices were also pretty low there, especially since Jotunheim wasn't all that far away. Jotunheim was a blue-collar mill town located on the wrong side of the tracks, not exactly an upscale place. Its residents were almost all giants, except for miscellaneous trolls, stray dogs, loan sharks, and other nasty characters. About the only things Jotunheim had going for it were the championship Jotunheim football team and Utgard-Loki's Pool Hall.

When the Æsir arrived, they found a bunch of country bumpkins called the Vanir sort of making a living there. The Vanir mostly raised grain, made moonshine and love, and held quilting bees on the weekend. Not exactly sophisticated folks. So the Æsir bought up most of the desirable real estate and went on a building spree. Among the cultural refinements sponsored by the Æsir were the Opera House, an addition to the Vanaheim Memorial Library (which had originally been a log cabin with about a dozen books on agriculture, a complete Danielle Steel collection, a Sears catalog, and the repair manual for a Farmall Cub tractor), the flush toilet, and The Valhalla Sports Bar and Grill.

The Æsir were big on ideas, but not so hot at architectural engineering and construction. So they hired the Acme Construction Company from Jotunheim to do the work, and also to surround the town with a nice 20-foot fieldstone wall with concertina wire on top, so's to keep out the riffraff. The Acme Construction Company turned out to be one Jotun named Bruno, his Clydesdale stallion Svadilfari, and a heavy-duty wagon mounted on truck tires. Bruno promised that he could build a bombproof security system with a lifetime warrantee for the Æsir over a period of three years, but he wanted the sun, the moon, and Freyja . . . he'd *heard* about Freyja . . . as payment. Odin didn't want to accept this offer at first, but Loki argued him into it. Odin didn't know that Bruno was Loki's uncle.

After all the haggling was done, the final contract read that all work had to be completed during the space of one year to the second, or Bruno'd forfeit all payment. Bruno also had to come up with all the materials himself. None of the Æsir thought that Bruno had a Chinaman's chance of completing the job in that time, and that they'd get most of a decent wall built gratis. Odin always was one cheap son-of-a-gun.

So Bruno and Svadilfari set to work. Since he wasn't Union, he could work overtime, weekends, and holidays without getting paid extra. Being magical, neither the horse or giant even needed to sleep, eat, or go to the bathroom. The image of Freyja in a hot-pink teddy with ostrich-feather trim was enough to make Bruno work like a beaver. The sun and moon he could use for headlights on the wagon, so as to make night jobs easier. He could also use them to jacklight deer.

It was amazing how much rock one giant and one Clydesdale could move. So much rock got moved, and so quickly was the wall getting built that Odin started to get worried. After all, he didn't own either the sun or the moon, and *nobody* owned Freyja.

11

Ol' "One-Eye" began to sweat, and that meant that he and the boys went looking for Loki. When they finally cornered him, there was a short discussion about how to pay off the giant, and how the Æsir might weasel out of this payment. Since a blowtorch was involved in this discussion, Loki hastily agreed to Do Something to Gum Up the Works.

Now Loki was the one sweating. He had to come up with something, fast. There was less than a day remaining in the stipulated time, but one more wagon-load would finish the job. And Svadilfari looked as fresh as the day he'd begun hauling rocks. He couldn't tell his uncle to muff the job, because Bruno was already planning the wedding. He couldn't slash the tires on the wagon, because they were police issue and didn't go flat. Wrecking the wagon would take too much time and make too much noise. And Bruno, who'd been lifting boulders for a year, wasn't exactly someone to tangle with, especially if one was a weedy punk like Loki. The clock was ticking; time was running out.

Odin, who'd been watching what was going on, saw Loki head for the woods at a flat-out run. "Damn", he thought, "now I have to go break the news to Freyja and hope that I can get out of range in time! I knew I shouldn't have trusted that weasel!" But then Odin's pet ravens, Hugin and Munin, came streaking out of the woods and slammed to a halt on his shoulders. After Odin had gotten their claws out of his skin and had calmed down a bit, the ravens whispered in the god's ears. Stereo. Somehow their news cheered Odin up so much that he sent the ravens to fetch the Einherjar and any other of the boys who wanted to see something interesting.

Meanwhile, back in the woods, Loki pulled a Superman-in-the-phonebooth gambit and changed himself into a mare in heat. A gorgeous mare, gloriously in heat. Nothing like pheromones as a distraction agent, Loki thought. He'd also had the foresight to become a Thoroughbred so that he could outrun the Clydesdale if things got too interesting. Then (s)he pranced out of the woods and flipped his/her tail at Svadilfari just as the stallion was coming back with the last load of boulders.

Well, children, let me tell you that Bruno got one heckuva surprise, you betcha! Svadilfari got one sniff and one look at his

13

wildest dream come true, and took off after Loki. Which meant that the wagon, its load of boulders, and Bruno also took off after Loki. Odin, meanwhile, took out a stopwatch. Time was running out on the contract, and if Bruno managed to get the bit out of Svadilfari's teeth, the giant might still get the job finished in time. He was certainly sawing back and forth on the reins with all his considerable strength, and might just get control of his horse yet.

Loki saw what was happening and slowed down just enough to give Svadilfari another good look and whiff. Needless to say, the stallion went out of his mind, and didn't pay the least attention to Bruno or anything else. Loki streaked toward the woods and leaped the horizontal trunk of a giant fallen oak-tree with Svadilfari hot on his/her tracks. The wagon hit the trunk, which was easily some twelve feet in diameter, and stopped cold. The harness and reins snapped, so Bruno stopped cold, too. The boulders, obeying the laws of momentum, did not. Svadilfari, freed of his multi-ton load, could now *really* run, and it didn't take him long at all to catch Loki. Bruno was left using some mighty naughty language and trying to dig his way out of a pile of boulders and splintered wood.

Meanwhile, atop the almost-completed section of wall, Odin and the boys watched the last seconds tick away on the stopwatch. The last second came and went . . . and the Acme Construction Company was now in default on the terms of the contract! That meant no sun, no moon, and *certainly* not Freyja for Bruno. After a few high-fives and rebel yells, the whole crew repaired to The Valhalla to celebrate, and Odin could once again breathe easy.

For some reason, nobody saw Loki at all during the next nine months or so. Sif said that she hoped the little twerp had finally bought the farm. Heimdall went around looking smug, but absolutely refused to reveal what he'd seen . . . after all, Heimdall's sight (and information sources) were far superior even to those of Odin's see-all, tell-all pet ravens. You never knew when you needed a tasty bit of blackmail information, and Heimdall wasn't about to spill the beans just to titillate the masses.

Loki finally showed up again the next spring with a strange expression on his face and half-leading, half-dragging a grey colt. There was something really odd about that colt, too; he had far too many feet. So many, that the poor thing was having trouble even walking. Every time he tried to step forward, those eight legs would form a Celtic knotwork pattern and the colt would have to stop, sort things out, and try again. Eventually they reached the main entrance to The Valhalla, where Freyja was avidly watching Balder ride the coin-operated bucking bull. Some of the Einherjar, who'd been watching Freyja watching Balder, noticed Loki and started chucking empties at him, since he and that crazy colt were blocking their view.

Thor and Frey, who had been playing stud poker with Odin, joined in the fun by adding pickled eggs to the missile mix. One egg hit Freyja right in the . . . well, this is a family story, and anyway, it's getting late. When the brawl was over, Loki had vamoosed again with Freyja, brandishing a cleaver, hot on his trail. That left Odin, Thor, Balder, and the Einherjar looking at this motherless waif of a confused, pitiful scrap of odd-looking horseflesh. Odin, the ever-canny businessman, realized that this could be a hot thing as a sideshow attraction at The Valhalla, so he quickly grabbed a bottle of Troll's Delight which he splashed onto the colt's back, naming him Sleipnir, claiming him as his own. After all, as Mayor, Odin could determine the ownership of abandoned, salvageable goods. And, since the aforesaid abandoned goods was standing mournfully in the middle of the bar-room of The Valhalla Sports Bar and Grill, the owner of that establishment (Odin) would be the logical person to take possession. The town magistrate (Odin) was also entirely agreeable to this solution.

And so, children, that's how Asgard was built and how Odin got a horse. Now go to sleep, and if you're good, Uncle Einar will tell you another story tomorrow night.

Chapter 2

HOW TYR GOT HIS PURPLE HEART

Do I have a story for you tonight! It sorta begins with Loki, but then most of the wilder things that happen in Asgard begin with Loki. He'd been lipping off to some of the boys as to how he was the trickiest sonuva bee in the known world. He could get away with *anything*, he declared somewhat soddenly. If you haven't guessed by now, Loki'd had his nose in the jug for a few hours, and he really didn't have the tolerance enjoyed by the habitués of The Valhalla Sports Bar and Grill. In fact, Loki got plowed on less than one six-pack, which in those parts was a serious handicap.

The boys all agreed on one thing, that Loki was a real sonuva bee, yah sure! So when this stray mutt came prowling around out back of The Valhalla's kitchen, tipping over garbage cans and chasing off the rats, the grill cook declared that surely this was Loki's son come looking for Daddy. Tyr, who was still a commissioned officer in the Army, said he felt sorry for the mangy cur and that it reminded him of a few of the enlistees he'd had to train for ROTC. At that time, Tyr still liked dogs.

Tyr decided that he'd feed the mutt up and train him for police work. It would be handy to have a good attack dog on the premises in case some of the trolls or Jotuns from across the river got over the Asgard Wall on mischief bent. He picked out a good threatening-sounding name, *Fenris*, and got the grill cook at The Valhalla to save bones, gristle and other offal. Tyr would be the only one to feed Fenris, as this would theoretically bond the dog to the man. Or so the AKC handbook said.

Fenris cleaned up beautifully, and when his mange was gone he turned out to be part wolf, part Rottweiler, and part something else that neither Tyr nor the AKC book could identify. He had a real aptitude for attack dog training. He could also talk, which was quite unusual for a dog. Tyr took him for long walks, training him to "alert" at strangers and false moves. Fenris eagerly threw

19

himself into his schooling, and was happiest when Tyr actually found some miscreant for him to gnaw on. Word got out among the criminal element that Fenris was bad news.

The chow supplied by The Valhalla kitchen was plentiful and frequent, and Fenris started to grow. He got bigger than your usual wolf, and then bigger than a wolf standing on the back of a Rottweiler. He also began to get an attitude.

Tyr soon realized that even he couldn't retain control over Fenris much longer. So far, Fenris still obeyed him and went on the long training walks with no problems. But his comments about the other inhabitants of Asgard began to worry Tyr. And Tyr did not take to being worried well.

Tyr mentioned his concerns to the mayor (Odin) and the town magistrate (Odin). The former suggested that Tyr consult a profiler, someone who could predict the animal's future behavior. The latter agreed, and said that the best in town was a 3-woman team who operated the "Wierd Sisters Occult Bookshop and Tea Room (Fortunes Told!)" which was located near Idunn's place. It was perfectly OK for Tyr to just go striding across the street in full uniform to a fortune teller. Remember, this was Asgard, not New England.

Urd, Verdandi and Skuld Norn were always pleased when a single, eligible male came into their shop. Since they were of different generations, there was always a Norn of the appropriate age on hand. Grandma Norn specialized in crystal ball and flame scrying, Verdandi generally read Tarot or palms, and Skuld, the youngest, was into New-Age rune tiles, Celtic Tree Goddess Oracle Cards, and the like. There was something for everybody.

Tyr elected to buy a horn of Greymalkin Full-Moon Witchin' Tea. He managed to gag most of it down, and then he handed the horn over to Verdandi. She swirled the dregs around and inverted the horn over a specially-marked saucer and then leaned over to examine the patterns formed by the soggy bits of tea leaf. Then she whistled long and low.

Skuld and Urd dropped what they were doing (in this case, knitting) and scurried over to see what Verdandi was looking at. Then they, too, whistled long and low. Tyr began to look even more worried and even (though he'd never admit it) faintly scared.

"Oh, my, you came to us *just* in time!" said Urd.

"*Just* in time!" echoed Skuld.

"Tomorrow would have been much, *much* too late!" murmured Verdandi, looking up into Tyr's eyes. "Fenris is due to go berserk tonight at midnight on the dot, and he's fated to tear down Asgard . . . all of it . . . after wrecking The Valhalla and slaughtering Odin and as many of the Einherjar as he can get his jaws on!"

"Oh, fudge (or similar words)!" exclaimed a now-alarmed Tyr, "What'n blazes would he do *that* for? Haven't we taken him in, fed him, and given him quality time?"

"The tea leaves don't lie," said Urd flatly, "My crystal ball agrees with them!"

"So does the Gardnerian I Ching!" quavered Skuld, "And it *never* likes to reveal secrets!"

Tyr swallowed hard. It was difficult to argue with such clear military intelligence. Fenris had to be nailed down and fast. It was time to activate Plan Delta Zulu Nancy. Tyr thanked the ladies and double-timed it back to HQ. Fortunately, the coast was clear. Fenris was not around. He requisitioned the heaviest hawser he could find in the procurement manual, emergency crash rush, from Dwarf and Dwarf Military Supplies. They made the best chain, and could do it fast and get it delivered by noon for only a moderate overrun in price. The dwarves were as good as their word, and at 11:59:59 a.m. Tyr received 100 feet of Part #68357-AQ titanium-steel 1 ton test chain. And it only cost $250/foot.

Tyr hustled over to The Valhalla and rounded up some of the troops. He also rounded up an entire ham from the cook (he'd told Odin what the Norns had said, and Odin told Tyr that this was now classified information and that he shouldn't tell the boys because that might alarm them). Tyr grumped about the modern army and lack of spine and what is this world coming to? Then he went out into the middle of Main Street and called Fenris.

Before long, Fenris showed up. Tyr's bellowing had a long range, but the smell of that ham had an even longer range. And it took a lot of meat to feed a dog the size of a Percheron.

"Hey, Fenris old boy, we're going to learn something new today!" said Tyr confidently, "This here ham says you can't get free if we tie you up with this chain!"

"Oh, yeah?" growled the wolf/?/Rottweiler, "Put up or shut up!"

Tyr laid the ham down on the road after the boys got 99 feet of the chain wrapped around Fenris. The wolf/?/Rottweiler gave one grunt and one heave, and suddenly everyone was ducking broken links of chain which whined and snarled off in all directions at nearly supersonic speed. The ham disappeared just as quickly. Fenris then gave a short, barking laugh and headed off toward Jotunheim. Tyr dashed back to HQ, got the dwarves on the horn, complained of shoddy merchandise, and got a promise of delivery of twice as much chain of twice the strength of the last lot by 1400 hours that day.

The dwarves were prompt, but required another $300/foot restocking fee. After all, a poor military contractor has to live, they protested. Tyr had to have the chain, so he paid the dwarves again. And once again the troops came out onto Main Street, this time with a whole sheep carcass. Tyr called Fenris who came running. He liked lamb even more than pork. And again the boys wrapped the chain around Fenris, this time welding the links together. And once again the wolf/?/Rottweiler just grunted, heaved, and broke the chain into individual links. He then grabbed the meat and jogged back off towards Jotunheim.

"(*Really* naughty language without one repeat for about 5 minutes)!" screamed Tyr, "(and more of the same)! Those (unprintable) dwarves better get with the program! (Expletive deleted)!!!"

So Tyr called the dwarves, who apologized and promised this new Kevlar-steel-neutronium alloy chain, delivery time 1600 GST. At only a $500/foot restocking fee. Tyr signed the contract, the dwarves delivered, and the boys came out onto Main Street carrying a whole ox. Tyr called Fenris, who liked beef even more than lamb. The boys took almost half an hour this time, using a laser torch to weld each link to all its neighbors, and the whole mass to about 30 old engine blocks which had been peacefully rusting away in back of The Valhalla. This oughta hold him, they opined.

Wrong-o. It took Fenris two grunts and three heaves, but he stepped out of the pile of scrap metal, grabbed the ox, and headed off back towards Jotunheim.

Oh my, children, what language Tyr used! It was so frightful that it caused the very sky to turn blue, and it is still blue to this day! The dwarves said that unfortunately technology only went so far, and until there was a major breakthrough in the tensile strength of metallic alloys, there was nothing more that they could do.

Odin, who had absolutely no intention of being slaughtered at midnight, sent his ravens out to get any information they could. Hugin and Munin were good at their job, so good that in today's market they could call their own tune as industrial spies. They came back with *nada*. Skirnir, Frey's publicist, then moseyed down to Alfheim where his good friends the elves and fairies lived. He came back with an entirely new ultra-high-tensile-strength material which would make steel chain obsolete.

This was their last shot. It was an unprepossessing thing, this satiny pink ribbon. Tyr sniffed and grumbled, Odin was incredulous, and the ravens fell off his shoulders backwards laughing. Everyone in The Valhalla came out to look at this marvel which only cost $7,500/foot. The grill cook brought out a huge vat of Thermonuclear Disaster Buffalo Wings and set it down in the middle of the road.

"This is the best I can do", he said, "As it is, until I get another delivery we're down to nachos, pretzels, peanuts, and chips!"

"Oh, well, here goes nothing!" mumbled Tyr. He called Fenris once more, and since it was not yet midnight Fenris obediently and quickly came. When he saw the ribbon, he dug in his paws and said, "No way! I ain't gonna have you guys put something like *that* on me! It looks like it was made by a buncha fairies!" "Hey!" blurted out Skirnir, "some of my best friends are fairies! Don't be such a homophobe!" "I ain't a homophobe, I just hate fairies!" growled Fenris, "Actually, I bet people would taste pretty good!"

It took a bit of negotiation, but Fenris finally allowed the boys to tie him up with the ribbon on two conditions. One, that Tyr would put his right hand in his mouth, as a pledge that he could get free OK. It was 11:32 p.m., and he still sortof trusted Tyr. Second, that nobody would *ever* tell anybody else about this dressup party with pink ribbon and such. Tyr had a bad feeling about this deal, but he knew that a military man had to Bite The Bullet and Stand Up To The Call. It was courage like this that separates heroes from men. Or gods, in this case.

When the boys finished their knotwork, the only thing you could see of Fenris were his eyes and mouth (which was closed on Tyr's hand). Houdini couldn't have gotten out of that one . . . and neither could Fenris. He lunged and grunted and heaved and moaned . . . and was still tied up. The only one who gave him a hand was Tyr.

When he came out of the anaesthesia, Tyr asked the doctor (Odin) what the ribbon was made of. It would have serious military applications; just think of what could be done with it! Armor, aerospace, the list went on. But Odin just sighed as he pinned a Purple Heart on Tyr's pajama top. Seems that a whole pile of rare ingredients went into that ribbon, and they were all used up. The beards of women (well, they sure forgot about the dwarven ladies!), the roots of mountains (mountains didn't have to grow like plants anyway), the sinews of a bear (and believe me, those weren't easy to get! Ever try to de-sinew a grizzly?), the breath of a fish (technically speaking they breathe water, said Njord, and they can still burp air bubbles, so I think someone was pulling your leg there!), the sound of a cat's footfall (here, Freyja broke into hysterical laughter . . . anyone who has cats *knows* about "kitty thunder") and the spittle of birds (glad they missed ravens, spat Hugin and Munin) all bound up with one heckuva world-class magical spell. Hey, it worked!

Midnight came, and Fenris' attitude underwent a dramatic shift to the downright bestial. But he was tied up good and tight, so Asgard, Odin, and most of the Einherjar were still standing as of 1 a.m. Somehow they managed to work the ribbon into a collar and leash, and Fenris was bound to a hastily-erected cinderblock and concrete doghouse out in back of The Valhalla. He howls when rain or hail falls on the corrugated tin roof, and he'll continue howling off and on, especially when people chuck empties at him, until the end of Time.

So that, children, is how Tyr lost his hand and had to retire on his disability pension, and how The Valhalla got a garbage Dispos-All which never breaks down. Now go to sleep, and if you're good, I'll tell you another story tomorrow night.

Chapter 3

THE BIG HEIST

O n one of the few occasions that Loki was actually in something resembling a state of good standing with the Æsir, he was invited to go on a hike and picnic with Odin and Hoenir. No wives, ravens, wolves, or girlfriends; this was going to be a "guy's day out". Loki tossed some running shoes in his backpack just in case . . . as well as a spare sweatshirt, swimming trunks, a loaded Mauser, loaded dice, and some trail mix. He'd recently had a good run, financially speaking, at Utgard-Loki's Pool Hall showing some of the younger Jotuns this little game of "chance". As a result, his color-coordinated hiking gear and outfit was top-of-the-line, from the most recent LL Bjørn catalog. When Loki was flush, he liked to live *large*.

He met up with Odin and Hoenir outside The Valhalla. Odin wore his usual ratty running suit, moth-eaten blue cloak, John Deere baseball cap, and scuffed Timberline boots. Gungnir, Odin's huge old-fashioned spear, was in his right hand; it also doubled as a dandy hiking staff. Hoenir, by contrast, wore camouflage battle-dress, a Fritz helmet, army boots, and a 125-pound backpack.

Hoenir always liked to Be Prepared, as You Never Knew What Would Happen.

Off they went across Bifrost Bridge towards Jotunheim and the lands beyond. Heimdall tried hard to keep a straight face as this ill-assorted trio showed him their commuter passes, but after they were out of earshot, he had himself a good hearty belly-laugh. Here was the Mayor going around looking like some old drifter, Loki looking like a magazine ad, and Hoenir pretending to be G.I. Joe!

The hikers struck out cross-country, cutting around north of Jotunheim, heading towards Midgard. Some good climbing mountains were located in Midgard, notably one called "Mount Everest". *That* should do for a nice spring stroll, Odin opined. And since they were gods, they wouldn't need extra oxygen, Sherpas, or to follow the "tourist track" used by the "summer people". As they headed for the hills, they chatted about this and that. Actually, Hoenir didn't say a thing, but that was OK since both Odin and Loki were great talkers. It would have been hard for *anyone* to get in edgewise when those two were having a gabfest.

They had just reached the foothills when Loki asked when they'd stop for the picnic part, and what was for dinner? Odin looked surprised, since he'd assumed Loki'd brought the eats. Hoenir then swung his pack off his back, opened it, and set out three MREs on a flattish rock.

"*That's* not food!" Loki objected, and "Gaah! I had to choke down far too many of *those* things in the Army!" growled Odin. Hoenir merely shrugged and stolidly started eating his own portion. Loki idly looked at the label to see if was remotely edible, but "Lutefisk, Beans, and Lard" didn't qualify in his book. Or in Odin's. Time to do a little hunting.

So, while Hoenir chowed down on the other MREs, Loki and Odin split up and started looking for something to eat. Even a MacDonald's would do. Loki stumbled across a small herd of yaks, and actually got one with his Mauser. He dragged the carcass back to "camp", but that was about as far as his culinary skills went. Hoenir skinned it out and field-dressed it, and then he and Odin went out hunting for firewood to cook the beast. Loki, meanwhile, had kept clear of the messy part as his clothes were new; besides, he had to clean his pistol.

It took a while for Odin and Hoenir to find enough wood to cook an entire yak. Even skinned out and field-dressed, one of those babies came in at more than 200 pounds. But eventually the gods had a pretty big pile of wood. Hoenir got out a small flamethrower to start the blaze, and Odin tossed the meat onto the roaring pyre. Nothing like napalm to get things going in a hurry. And by now, Loki and Odin were very, very hungry.

The meat smelled delicious as it cooked, and even Hoenir began to look hungry. Odin stirred the wood so'd it would blaze even hotter. He wanted dinner *right now*! Back at The Valhalla, there was always food whenever you wanted it; but here, Odin had to wait until it was ready.

Finally, he could stand it no longer. He pulled the meat out of the fire with his spear, and then hunkered down with his Buck knife at the ready. But the meat was still almost raw, and Odin liked his medium well-done.

"I musta been too eager," he said, "Hoenir, toss this back in the fire, and jazz it a bit, hey?"

Hoenir did so, loosing a 5-second stream of flaming napalm directly at the meat at point-blank range. Odin and Loki had to jump back before they lost eyebrows, whiskers, and other important things. About fifteen minutes later, when the flames had died down to a mere 4 feet, Odin again hauled the roast out of the fire. It was still almost raw. And the cool of evening was settling in, with a hint of coming snow.

Odin, wizard that he was, smelled magic in the air. That meat should have been crispy well-done. And he could still almost hear it moo. Or whatever yaks said.

"Hocus, pocus, come to focus, That which hinders me!" he recited while waving Gungnir around in what looked like intricate Cabbalistic figures. As a hiking stick, that spear made a dandy wizard's staff. And as its head blazed like a klieg light, a gigundo eagle suddenly popped into sight. It had been invisible, sitting next to the now-empty MRE tins on the flattish rock, watching the proceedings with its beady yellow eyes.

Now it opened its beak and said, "Give me first crack at the meat, and I'll unhex it so's it can get cooked the rest of the way!"

A talking eagle was a novelty in Midgard, but Asgard was full of talking birds, trees, rocks, slugs, etc. so the trio weren't taken back by this sudden outburst. A quick confab was held, and the gods agreed to the eagle's request. After all, how much meat can an eagle hold?

They soon found out. All of it, except for the bones, a few scraps of gristle and tendon, the tail, the hooves, and the head. Loki was so mad at this that he took a swing at the bird with his new All-Terrain Hiking Stick, Model 2437-A. It hit the eagle square on its back, knocking it off the remains of the carcass and also into flight. Surprise! As the eagle climbed into the air, the stick stuck fast to its body, and Loki was stuck fast to the stick. The eagle didn't seem at all bothered by that arrangement as it flew higher, heading towards the rugged face of Mount Everest. It seemed to delight in bouncing Loki off some of the more spectacular razor-ridges and swathes of gravelly scree while Loki hollered, threatened, cussed, and pleaded to be released. The eagle finally deigned to notice his passenger after Loki had snagged between a pair of close-set jagged boulders and almost didn't scrape through. Needless to say, Loki's new clothes were a mess.

"OK, wise guy, I'll let you live on one condition", the eagle screeched as it headed for another rock face. Loki, having been "snap-the-whipped" into far too many rock faces at this point, weakly agreed to do anything the eagle wanted. *Any*thing . . . .

The eagle (whose name *wasn't* Sam, by the way) told Loki that he was to have Idunn, complete with her basket of golden apples, on the Jotunheim side of the Bifrost Bridge in exactly one week's time. At high noon. On the dot. Or else. And Loki agreed. The eagle dropped him from a mere 34-foot altitude onto a rubble-field and flew away. Loki then realized that he'd been had by a Jotun in disguise . . . could it have been that chap he'd "won" all that money from the other day?

Anyhow, a very battered Loki finally straggled into camp, where the others were waiting for him. He didn't say anything about the deal he'd made with the eagle, because Odin and Hoenir would finish the job the eagle had started. And Loki really valued his own skin.

Well, children, Loki had a whole week to hatch his plans. He went into "The Golden Apple" at about 11:30 a.m. on the fateful day, and asked Idunn if she had any aqua regia for his bruises. Idunn, that kind soul, ooo'd and oh'd over him, and got out her homeopathy kit.

"How'd you get so black and blue?" she asked, "What were you protesting? Did the right-wing Establishment goons hurt you very badly?"

"Nope, missed the 'Save the Red-Spotted Snail Darter' protest because I'd found this huge apple tree . . . it must be more'n three hundred years old! And it's loaded with apples which look *just* like yours! I'd climbed up to get one, but I fell off a branch, which is why I look like this. But you oughta come see this tree! Quickly, because the fella who owns it is planning to chop it down for pulpwood at twelve noon today! And, hey, you might bring *your* apples along so's you could compare them on the spot to the ones on this tree!"

That was enough for Idunn. That such a venerable, productive member of the plant kingdom was about to be slaughtered in cold sap by an unscrupulous money-grubbing "farmer" who probably also used DDT in secret, got her blood boiling. She grabbed a blank protest sign, scribbled "Save The Tree!" in huge red runes on it, and took off with Loki across Bifrost Bridge. Loki made very sure that Idunn also brought her basket of apples along.

33

No sooner had they gotten across the bridge and over the Midgard border, when the eagle pounced on Idunn and carried her off, kicking and screaming. Loki pretended to run for help, but he was actually just Getting Out Of Dodge. The eagle flew to its castle home in Jotunheim, where it changed into a very large, mean, ugly Jotun named Thjazi. He handcuffed Idunn to an iron pipe, and set her box of apples on his coffee table (crate) in front of his TV.

"Haw, haw, haw!" he laughed, "Now I have you, and your little apples, too! All mine!" And he laughed even louder when Idunn wept and pleaded to be released, apples and all. For her apples were special, they granted everlasting life. She stocked them for the Æsir and Vanir, not for some ecologically-unfriendly chauvinist pig of a Jotun.

"I think I'll eat all the apples during the Jotunheim football game, which is coming on now, and save you for half-time. I'll be ready for . . . *dessert* . . . then," he leered brutishly. Idunn shrank back and began to try to become One With The Universe so that the White Light Of Truth And Justice would Shine, and she could Tell Someone—*anyone* in Asgard—that she'd been kidnapped and was in imminent danger.

Meanwhile, back in Jotunheim, nobody missed Idunn at first. But when Skirnir noticed that he was getting "frownie" wrinkles, he went over to Idunn's place only to be met by a "Out For Lunch" sign. Skirnir alerted Frey, who admitted that he'd been having a little problem lately, and that he'd had to resort to Viagra. Frigg stormed into The Valhalla looking for her husband (he wondered who this old bat was, and she wondered who that ancient geezer behind the counter was) and demanded action, now! She was going to have the Ladies' Bridge Club in tomorrow, and she couldn't *possibly* look like this when the ladies came, and where was her daily apple? Balder followed her in, but he only wanted a mug of warm milk and to sit by the fire. Puff and Fluff, Freyja's cats, jumped up onto the counter and started yowling at the Mayor (Odin) and the Town Magistrate (Odin) to Do Something. The ravens agreed; Odin's shoulders had gotten too bony to sit on comfortably. The gods were getting older by the minute; grey hair replaced thick glossy blond(e)/brown/auburn/black/red manes and whiskers. Idunn and her magic apples had to be found, and *fast*.

Thor hobbled in. His bald head shone in the light of the neon beer signs, and his long grey beard was falling out in patches. He looked owlishly around at the assembled crowd.

"Where the (subterranean region noted for thermal activity) is Loki???" he wheezed, "Dollars to doughnuts *he's* behind this!"

"I saw him and Idunn go across the bridge," an ancient Heimdall creaked, "I didn't see her come back, though, come to think of it. I think we better round up a posse and go looking for him now, before we all get Alzheimer's!"

And so a posse of the spryest Æsir and Vanir headed out looking for Loki. It took a while (the posse kept getting older and losing members), but eventually Loki was found rifling through Idunn's cash box at her store. Hoenir and Tyr each held an Uzi on him while Heimdall fumbled a set of handcuffs onto his wrists. The three gods then escorted Loki down to The Valhalla, where the Einherjar were getting ready to hold a good old-fashioned neck-tie party.

"Court is in session!" said Odin in an asthmatic voice, "All rise. No need or time to bother with the formalities of testimony; I'm hereby declaring Loki guilty before, during, and after the fact, which is kidnapping, risk of injury, willful negligence, and malicious intent to murder. The penalty is death. String him up, boys!"

"*No, wait*!!!" screamed Loki, "I was forced into it!" And the whole story came out. For once, Loki told it straight. Odin said the court'd pardon Loki only if he got Idunn and her apples back safe and unharmed. So Loki borrowed Freyja's Corvette and headed off to Jotunheim. He was terrified, but this was his only chance to redeem his life. Heimdall had put one of those unbreak-able monitoring bracelets on Loki's ankle, so the Feds knew exactly where he was and what he was doing at all times. They'd also wired that bracelet with a miniaturized one-megaton nuke, so if Loki blew it, Loki'd become radioactive fallout.

When Loki got almost to Thjazi's house, he parked the 'Vette facing back towards Asgard. He snuck across the lawn, missing the land mines by sheer luck, and pried open a back window. He heard cheering noises inside, and worried that he'd come too late and that Idunn had been hurt or worse. But as he poked his head cautiously around the corner, he saw that it was only the TV blasting the football game at high volume. And Thjazi wasn't there. Idunn and her apples, however, were.

Loki picked the lock on the handcuffs and quickly scooped up both Idunn and the fruit. He thought he heard the toilet flush, so he scooted out the window, tucking a bag of peanuts into his pants pocket. What? Oh, Loki was a shape-changer, children, and he'd temporarily changed Idunn and her apples into a packet of Mr. Peanut dry-roasted nuts. That made her a lot more portable than if she was a people. And there wouldn't be the danger of losing apples all over the place if he had to run for it. He hopped into the Corvette and gunned it. But above the full-throated roar of the Corvette's magnificent engine, he could hear Thjazi's fire-whistle scream. The Jotun had instantly noticed that he'd been robbed.

Loki peeled out of there, breaking every speed law there ever was, including that of light. Hot on his exhaust came Thjazi, this time disguised as an F-15 Eagle armed with heat-seeking air-to-ground missiles.

Meanwhile, back at the ranch (or, in this case, Asgard), the gods got out the heavy artillery and turned the spotting radar (actually, Urd's crystal ball) to "search" mode. Tyr and the VFW boys poured napalm mixed with powdered magnesium into the moat outside the Asgard Wall, and stood ready with flamethrowers so's they could ignite it on cue at just the right time.

Loki screamed over the Bifrost bridge so fast that he nearly achieved escape velocity when he popped over its hump. The Corvette sailed over the Wall and landed as lightly as a bird at Freyja's feet. And as the Eagle screamed in for the kill, Tyr and the boys let 'er rip. And so it was, for Thjazi. R.I.P. The Eagle caught fire and became a sort of meteorite, flaring brilliantly before it hit the ground in back of the Hell-Hole Funeral Home.

6-SIBL

And that, children, is how Idunn was stolen and rescued, and why Hela has that wierd modern-art metal sculpture out behind her place. The gods all got their apple a day again, and became their own proper ages. And Loki, who hadn't put a scratch on the Corvette, was sentenced to merely five years on parole, with time off for good behavior.

So now, children, it's time to go to sleep. And Uncle Einar might just mosey down to the kitchen and see if there's any of your Mom's apple pie left!

Chapter 4

FREYJA'S LITTLE SECRET

What's this? You want a *romantic* story? Are you feeling all right? Oh, well, I suppose I have a good romantic story on hand, one about Freyja. It couldn't be much of a romantic story if Freyja *weren't* in it. She's always either falling in love, head-over-heels in love, or recovering from having been in love. What about Frey, you ask? I'll tell you one about *him* another time.

Well, once upon a time, Freyja saw this handsome prince. She didn't know if he actually *was* a prince or not, but he was your standard tall, blond, blue-eyed muscular, gorgeous hunk. Yes, I know that there are all colors and styles of hunks, but since this fellow was a Norseman, chances are he was a tall, blond, blue-eyed, and so forth hunk.

Freyja hadn't had an affair in weeks. She was desperate. And this young man looked as if he'd make an excellent boyfriend, even in spite of the fact that he was a mortal human being. And a computer programmer, at that. The Hunk was probably a virgin, too, she mused happily . . . .

So the first thing she did was to log on and Email him her picture. Subtle. He was interested, in sort of an academic way, in her stats (45-20-32) . . . he thought those numbers referred to her tennis game, however. As Freyja'd thought, this dreamboat was clueless and totally innocent. The goddess licked her lips slowly as she flipped through a Victoria's Secret catalog, looking for just the perfect negligée.

She also enrolled in a quickie "OS-1 For Beginners" class, followed by "Win95 For Idiots" at the Vanaheim Community College. She commissioned a Web Page, one of those kinds that get edited out by Net Nanny, and bought her own domain ("goodtimes.edu") . . . having an affair with Freyja was some educational, you betcha! And she found out that The Hunk was going to be at the NerdExpo Computer Show to be held at the Midgard Arena and Convention Center in one week.

Time to get into high gear. Falling in love is easy; the hard part is getting the object of one's affections to fall head-over heels in love with you. Careful preparations had to be made, research had to be done. The crate from Victoria's Secret arrived Overnight Express (Freyja had had a hard time deciding which filmy little nothing would be best, so she'd ordered one of everything). She stocked her 'fridge with caviar, paté de foie gras, champagne, Westphalian ham, and other such elegant goodies. Her cats, Puff and Fluff, were freshly bathed, brushed, and given new rhinestone collars. She put a white fitted sleeping-fur on the king-sized waterbed, a black silk top-sheet over that, and scattered about 30 small pink heart-shaped satin lace-edged pillows all about the room. The ceiling mirrors were polished, the 3"-deep pile cream shag carpet vacuumed, and the water in the sunken marble jacuzzi changed. As I said, Freyja did her homework, and was ready for Stage II just before the convention opened.

"What does a gorgeous hunk of a computer nerd like that look for in a girl?" Freyja asked herself, thinking hard and blowing on her freshly-polished nails. "The usual doesn't apply here. I have to get him interested in coming back to my place and staying for a while . . . and I suppose I ought to find out what his name is, too. I wonder what my Tarot says about this?"

That meant a trip to the Norns' place, and enduring the leers, knowing looks, snickers, nudges, etc. from the sisters. Urd brought up a picture of the "Target Hunk Prince" on her crystal ball, and all four women hungrily licked their lips. Freyja insisted that she had first dibs, so back off! He's *mine*! Her Tarot reading (Norse Cross layout) indicated great joy in the near future. Freyja was definitely psyched.

To make sure, the Norn sisters lit some incense, drank some fizzy orange potion, and inhaled various stupefying smokes in preparation for a spirit-writing séance. A clean linen tablecloth had been placed on the old round oaken table, and the four women joined hands. Skuld was the one to whom the vision came; she broke her grip and reached "Out" for quill and vellum. What she got, however, was a large "jewel box" containing 6 CDs, and a large paper-bound book.

"Win2010," she musingly read, " . . . Guaranteed Bug-Free . . . Released Only After Thorough Testing . . . ." She looked faintly puzzled as she handed the collection to Freyja. "I don't know what this is all about, but someone in the Spirit World seems to think that this is just what you need!"

Freyja'd had just enough computer training to realize that she'd gotten her hands on the perfect bait. "He'll see this, get really interested, and then I can lure him over to my place so's he can play with it . . . but it's going to be *me* he plays with . . . " she thought contentedly as she left the shop, " . . . And now to the Midgard Arena and Convention Center!"

The bait worked like a charm. Turned out the fellow's name was Ottar Insteinsson, and that he was an even more gorgeous hunk at close range. Freyja shivered in anticipation. Her hormones were all alert and ready. Only one more hurdle to leap, and then it would be time for hey, diddle diddle!

That hurdle was smuggling him past Heimdall. Now, Heimdall specifically targeted mortals among those he barred from crossing his bridge. He'd seen all sorts of ruses and tricks, but his data base was up to date and Freyja would have to think up something entirely new in order to get Ottar past him. Ottar, his heart-stoppingly beautiful blue eyes gazing lovingly at the CDs nestled in the crook of Freyja's pretty arm, was entirely agreeable to whatever she wanted.

Freyja made a few passes in the air with her free hand, and Presto! Bingo! Ottar was magically transformed into a white Lincoln Continental convertible with red leather interior trim. A real pig to drive, but elegant in its own way. Ottar, still mesmerized by this gorgeous vision he'd had, didn't notice anything unusual at all. Freyja drove slowly off, stopping a few blocks later to pick up some Twinkies at the corner store. She'd seen Twinkies wrappers littered all over the Convention Center floor, and wanted to make *absolutely* sure that Ottar would stay a while.

The woman at the counter was a grumpy old Jotun named Hyndla, who seemed to be perpetually mad at the world and everyone in it. She wore pink curlers in her ratty hair, a faded T-shirt with the words "Honkers Restaurant and Peep Show" strategically positioned on its front, and a large, black, cheap half-smoked cigar on her lower lip. She also had her own suspicions about that big car which just pulled up outside her shop.

"What'cher want?" the Jotun asked in a gravelly voice as Freyja came in the door, "Hey, nice wheels ya got out there! Betcha that set you back a bundle!"

"It's new," Freyja answered as she paid for a case of Twinkies, "The dealer said that it had a really smooth ride and would last forever!"

"*I* know what yer up to, missy!" Hyndla leered, "That ain't no real car, that's really a geek named Ottar who you've magicked into being a car! I know all *sorts* of things about that guy!"

"Oh? . . . er, that's just because the paint is new . . . it's just a car . . . um, what do you know about this Ottar?"

"Well, let me tell you!" cackled the old lady, happy to discover this new, tasty gossip item, "His Dad was an All-Star quarterback for the Vikings, and his Mom was in seminary school before she met her husband. Ottar went to the University of Minnesota, got his masters' at Harvard, and his first Ph.D. at MIT. The others are mostly from Berkeley, Yale, Stanford, and RPI. Smart fella . . . ." the giantess eyed Freyja knowingly, " . . . usually . . ."

"Oh, tell me more!" Freyja breathed, her bosom heaving as she clutched her case of Twinkies, "He sounds di*vine*!"

The headlights of the Continental seemed to twinkle almost as if alive. Hyndla's lips quirked around her cigar butt as she continued her recital.

"Yup, that's some car you got. Maybe I can ride it, too?"

"*No*!!!" Freyja hastily gasped, "I promised I wouldn't let *any*one else ride it! . . . and what *else* do you know about this hypothetical Ottar?"

"Oh, he has a whole raft of relatives. Every single one of 'em was the very best at what he or she did. Twelve of 'em competed in the Winter Olympics . . . they were the ice hockey team. I'm sure you've heard about *them*! Another relative named Sigurd was a famous opera singer and got to kill a dragon every night on stage. Lawmen, card-sharps, doctors, tinkers, spies . . . the lot of 'em were the very best in all the world at whatever they did!"

Freyja quickly scooped up her case of Twinkies and tenderly deposited it beside her on the front seat of the convertible, which followed her every move with its headlights. She was really glad she'd stopped here and found out about Ottar . . . now, if he were world-class at . . . *tra*, la, la . . . She barely glanced at Heimdall as she showed her commuter pass at the Bifrost toll booth. Heimdall, who was busy pasting up a new "Wanted!" poster for Loki, casually waved her on . . . and Freyja had cleared the final obstacle to bliss.

Nobody saw Freyja for quite a while. If anyone passed by her place, they noticed that things seemed to be happiness, light, and sunshine in that area, and that Puff and Fluff sat staring out the windows with fatuous smiles on their kitty faces. Heimdall, who'd seen perfectly well what the true nature of that car was, stored that fact in his expanding dossier . . . you never knew when you'd need a little scandalous blackmail . . . and he smiled contentedly as he ate some more popcorn and watched the black-and-white screen of the monitor which was receiving input from that little video camera he'd salted away behind the one-way mirror on Freyja's ceiling . . . .

Oops, I hear your Mom coming to kiss you goodnight! For heaven's sake, *please* don't tell her which story I told you children tonight! If she finds out, it'll be "Good-Bye, Uncle Einar!"

Chapter 5

HOW THOR LOST HIS HAMMER AND FREYJA DIDN'T GET HITCHED

O K, children, since you've been really good today, Uncle Einar will tell you the story of Thor's hammer and Freyja's near miss with wedded bliss. What kind of hammer did Thor have, you ask? No, it's not at all like Daddy's claw hammer. It's more sort of like a 6-pound short-handled sledge hammer. Because it had been made for a god, it was magical. It sorta glowed like the coals in a fireplace and, when thrown, it would always hit its target. Then it would boomerang back to Thor's hand, so's the god could throw it again. He'd gotten so good with that hammer that he could throw it faster than machine gun fire! Targets were usually trolls and giants and other such lowlife.

This hammer was named Mjollnir, and it was Thor's pride and joy. I think even more so than his Harley, and Thor purely *loved* that Harley. Hey, with Mjollnir in his fist, he could face down the biggest, meanest, baddest dude that ever walked, slithered, or flew. In fact, he'd go out looking for trouble when things got slow at the Thrudheim Athletic Club or at The Valhalla. Thor wasn't exactly what you'd call a great intellect, so the Library and the Opera House were out, entertainment-wise. Much more fun to fire up the Hog, roar on down to Jotunheim, and kick some serious ass.

Well, one morning Thor woke up and felt under his pillow where he kept Mjollnir. Nothing. No hammer. How he managed to sleep with only one pillow between the hammer and his head escapes me, but somehow he did. This morning, however, there was no comforting touch of solid metal under the pillow. The god then searched the entire room including the closet where his comic book collection and 10 years' worth of Hemming's Motor News were stored. This took a bit of time, since he wasn't the world's neatest person. No hammer.

Thor got mad. Now, when ordinary folks blow up, they stamp around, their faces get red, they wave their arms, and maybe they shout a bit. Thor was a god. When he got mad, things were measured by the Richter scale. If it weren't for the magical spells protecting the furniture and wallpaper, there would have been a major fire and/or flood in that room, so dramatic and emphatic was Thor's vocabulary. I mean, the god cussed up a real storm. Complete with tornadoes, lightning, hail, and thunder. Hugin and Munin, Odin's pet spies, heard what was going on and repeated the juicier bits to Odin.

Thor stomped down to The Valhalla looking for Loki. When anything went wrong, folks automatically looked for Loki. And this time, Loki was in for it, because Thor's hammer was Asgard's main defense against the trolls, giants, and other bad actors. As soon as that lot found out that Asgard was defenseless, they'd loot, pillage, plunder, burn, hack, slay, etc. until the place was reduced to a smoking, glassy-surfaced parking lot. Not even the famous wall would be able to keep them all out.

Heimdall and the ravens finally located Loki, who'd turned himself into a lampshade hoping to escape notice. Even without his hammer, Thor was nobody to be trifled with, so Loki gave up and turned back into a people. Thor grabbed Loki in what his sensai would call a totally dishonorable grip, and wrung the truth out of him. Seems Loki had needed some cash fast, thanks to a bad night over at Utgard-Loki's Pool Hall at the hands of one Thrym. Giants don't like to be owed money, especially by the likes of Loki. Nobody in their right mind would *ever* take an IOU from Loki. The deal was that Loki should filch Thor's hammer, and that the only way the Æsir could get the hammer back was for Freyja to marry Thrym. It was worth it to the giant to give the hammer back, if he could legally get his paws on Freyja. He'd *heard* about Freyja.

When Freyja heard the news, both Thor and Loki ducked fast. She was so mad at the pair of 'em that her neck swelled up and broke Brisingamen, her favorite necklace, showering beads all over the place. Her matched pair of "Fancy Feast" Persians tried to run under the waterbed (mistake) and knocked themselves out cold. Perfume bottles, loose shoes, throwing stars, pink satin pillows with lace trim, that sort of stuff was thrown about (mostly at Loki).

"No way, José! If you think I'm actually going to go *marry* a giant, you have another big fat thought coming!" Freyja screamed. Or words sort of like those, except that they made the plaster crack and Thor's beard begin to smoke. "You got yourselves into this mess, you just get yourselves out of it! Without me!"

Thor dragged Loki over to The Valhalla. He needed to get some advice from Odin, and a strong drink. Not necessarily in that order. Most of the other Æsir were already there, having heard the news from Heimdall, who'd just put out an "Extra" edition of the *Gjallarhorn Gazette*. The Einherjar were still chuck-

51

ling over some of the choicer epithets. Heimdall, being the god of editors, had been able to include Freyja's comments as well as the earlier remarks by Thor.

Well, to make a long story shorter, it was obvious to everybody that Thor's hammer had to be gotten back. Since the price was one bride, to wit, Freyja; and since Freyja flat-out refused to be tied to only one man (and especially to a Jotun), some other solution had to be found. Freyja even refused to loan Loki her candy-apple red Corvette with feather-glide cruise control to do a quick round-trip smash-'n'-grab. Loki was even worse on cars than that kid who was the valet parker at the Folkvang Hotel.

Heimdall came up with the suggestion that Thor go in drag as "Freyja" to Thrym's place and kootchy-koo him into handing over the hammer. The boys in the bar thought this was a dandy idea, and ran home to borrow makeup and frilly underwear from their wives and sweethearts. Thor had nearly swallowed his teeth when the verdict came down, which made the Einherjar laugh even more. Odin decreed that this was a national emergency, which meant a round or three of Triple-Ringed Tonsil Wash, with double rations to Thor in the hopes of anesthetizing him for the operation.

Back came the boys, dragging feather boas, old ball gowns, and a rather daring selection of undergarments. Freyja had calmed down by now, and was so amused by the idea of Thor dressing up to look like her that she loaned him her favorite necklace. That item had by now become quite accustomed to magically re-assembling itself after one of Freyja's temper tantrums. Heimdall was all for shaving Thor's beard, but the thunder god put his foot down hard on that suggestion (and on Heimdall).

The scene then began to resemble the part of Cinderella (the Disney movie) when the mice started dressing Cinderella for the ball. Clip-on rhinestone earrings dangled from Thor's ears. Peacock-blue eyeshadow, eyeliner, mascara, blusher, rouge, lipstick, the lot. And a few squirts of "My Sin" to top it off. Somehow they crammed Thor into one of Frigg's old girdles, which creaked alarmingly at the strain. It did give Thor sort of an hourglass figure . . . well, all right, he looked like a mattress tied around the middle with a rope . . . which was then covered with a wedding dress (size 45W). Panty hose, 4" heels, and a long opaque bridal veil which hung down in front to hide the beard. Actually, the veil was draped like an Indian *chadoor* which hides the face from the nose on down, so's Thor could see where he was going. Skirnir was particularly pleased with the job he'd done on Thor's eyes, and wanted the prospective bridegroom to appreciate their beauty as well. Finally, to top it off, Freyja placed Brisingamen around Thor's neck. The gods and goddesses all wished Thor and Loki "Bon Voyage" while trying to keep straight faces, and Heimdall let them cross the Bifrost Bridge without paying the toll. Some wag had even decorated Thor's Harley with white ribbons, pink silk rosebuds, and heart-shaped Mylar balloons. Thor was definitely *not* amused.

As I understand it, children, that was not a happy trip. Thor's gown kept getting caught in the Harley's rear wheel spokes, and then he'd get thrown off the bike, and then he'd go beat up Loki, and then climb back on again, and five minutes later the whole sequence began anew. Fortunately for Thor's disguise the dress was Scotch-Guarded, so most of the dirt and grease brushed off OK.

Eventually they reached Thrym's place, which was located in the back lot of the Jotunheim trailer park. The giants, having been alerted by a pair of congenial ravens, were just finishing up the preparations for the wedding. Every Domino's Pizza within 50 miles was cranking to capacity, and Chinese takeout delivery vans lined the street. Thrym had had a trailer-truckload of cold kegs delivered and set up on the patio, along with a couple of skids of pretzels and chips. A huge gumdrop surprise cake frosted with Kool-Whip was set up on sawhorses, and the Jotunheim Jazz Band (two bagpipes, a kettle drum, and a trombone) were warming up for the first set. It was clear that the giants had really gone all-out on this one.

When the bridal party roared up to the front door, the giant was ready and waiting. He'd somehow found a tux that almost fit, and had even brushed and greased his hair and beard. "Freyja" alit from the disguised Harley with as much grace as possible under the circumstances, while Thrym ogled "her" brawny legs. Loki, done up as a French maid, was ogled by the rest of the giants. And since Jotunheim weddings traditionally had the feast first, Thrym politely escorted "Freyja" straight to the food. Thor's appetite had been quite taken away by just looking at Thrym. Actually, anybody not a giant would have lost their appetites (if not lunch) if they looked at Thrym. "Ugly" doesn't even *begin* to cover it. I mean, he was so ugly that he'd passed being distinguished-looking and was back into ugly.

Pizza and *dim sum* and the probability of massive amounts of beer soon rallied "Freyja"'s appetite, and "she" began to shovel it in so fast that "her" fork made a sound like helicopter rotors. Thrym, startled when his bride drank a six-pack of kegs without even blinking, said "Hey, ya gonna be sober for later? And where'n hell ya puttin' all that chow? Leave some for the rest of the gang!"

"Ah, mon-soor, zee beeyoooteeful Freyja, shee has been so 'appee about zees wedding zat shee couldn't eat a *theeng* for zee last week!" piped up Loki.

Thrym was so overcome with desire at this, that he leaned over to plant a big smackeroo on his bride's lips. Before he'd gotten the veil more than halfway lifted, "Freyja" gave him such a megawatt laser look that the giant was thrown across the hall to land splat on the far wall.

"Whoa, baby, what'n hell ya looking at me like *that* for?" Thrym moaned as he picked himself up off the floor, "I'm almost yer husband!"

"Ah, mon-soor", warbled the crafty Loki, "Freyja's been sooo excited about you that she hasn't slept a single *weenk* in zee last week!"

"Hot-cha! Come to me, sweetcheeks!" burbled the giant as he gathered "Freyja" tenderly in his steely arms, "You'n'me gonna really get it on, you bet!"

"Hey, ain't we gonna have the preach' read a few (hic!) words first?" asked one of the more sober guests, "We gotta do this all legal, like, or them (burp!) Æsir'll come down here and rip you a new one!" Nobody ever said that giants were English (or in this case, Old Norse) scholars, or that they were noted for elegance or deportment.

"Yeah, let's do this proper", said another, "An' we even got a ceremonial wedding hammer to bless the bride'n'groom!" "Someone git th'hammer (hic!)!" "Hey, Thrym, where'dja hide it?" "Not down in the 7-mile-deep well, I hope?" "Oh. Down in the 7-mile-deep well. (Anglo-Saxon phrase of indelicate content)!" "Awright (hic!), who gonna climb down after that sucker?" "Ain't gonna be me, I gotta bone in my leg!" "Hey, (buuurrp!) Björn! You go for it!" "Twelve of us is Björn, which one ya want?" "Björn Thighsmasher, you're still standing, *you* go for it!" "Why izzit always me? I hadda go get the fried troll tripe last time!" "Sez you!" etc.

Well, it took a while, but finally things got sorted out and someone put the dripping-wet Mjollnir into Thrym's hairy fist. Thrym, who'd wedged himself onto a beat-up sofa with his intended, had been busy trying to get his arm around "her". Unsuccessfully, I might add. The preacher got ready to read the vows, and Thrym laid the hammer on "Freyja"'s knees with its handle suggestively pointed at "her" bellybutton.

"Eeeeee-haaaaah!" screamed the thunder-god in delight, sweeping his disguise off with the hand not grabbing Mjollnir, "Surpriiiiiise!" The sound effects immediately following this comment were mostly very loud crashes and sizzling noises, as of a large stone building being simultaneously slagged down and pounded into dust. And of a lot of drunk giants being turned into dead drunk giants.

And that, children, is how Thor found his hammer, and how Freyja didn't get hitched. And if you're extra-specially good, Uncle Einar will read you another story tomorrow night.

Chapter 6

THE DAY IT RAINED MEAD

Hullo, there, children! Your Mom says you've tried to be good today, so I 'll give you the benefit of the doubt, as well as another story. This one takes place a long, long, *long* time ago, back when Tyr was still an enlisted officer in the Army. Odin had just closed a real estate deal for some commercially zoned property on Main Street, and was in the process of applying for a liquor license. Yes, I know that this story comes earlier than the one I told you last night, but that's the way it goes.

Odin and Frigg were recent immigrants, as the old boy saw a real cash potential in setting up a proper watering hole in Asgard. Before The Valhalla opened, folks either brewed their own hooch or bought it from Fjalar and Galar, the local moonshiners. A singularly unsavory pair of dwarves, they sold their murky brew off the back of an ancient red pickup truck, and refused to tell anyone what their "secret ingredient" was. A Mongol Hordesman who'd been passing by said that this stuff tasted like kvass or kumiss, and he also told the townsfolk of Asgard just how kumiss was made. Odin got his money's worth from the Mongol, because after that, nobody wanted to buy from Fjalar and Galar. That took care of the competition.

The liquor license was hastily issued by the town magistrate (Odin, who'd just been elected), and The Valhalla opened its doors. Now, *that* was a party. Everybody in town came, including a few folks from across the bridge. Odin had every kind of potable adult beverage available out on the counter, and a merry time was had by all.

Fjalar and Galar, however, didn't take their business failure lightly. One of their Jotunheim acquaintances, a two-bit gangster named Gilling, was called in for consultation. Gilling and his wife ran an enforcement agency, and the dwarves thought that they might handle a little kneecapping job. Gilling blew it, so the dwarves took him for a short sea voyage. Unfortunately for the giant, the cement overcoat he wore kept him from returning to dry land with the dwarves.

Eleanora Sophia (née Garbanzo), Gilling's widow, smelled a rat and went to discuss things with her Family. Her uncle Guido suggested that Eleanora see to the dwarves with her famous arsenic soufflé. As she came to their door, somehow a load of concrete sewer pipe got dropped on her head, and so the Dwarf Affair landed back in Guido's lap. It happened that Gilling and Eleanora's son, Suttung, was undergoing the ceremony to become a "made man". If he could dispose of the dwarves quietly and cluelessly, this would stand in his favor.

Suttung was not someone you'd call subtle. He got through the dwarves' alarm system with thermite, and had Fjalar and Galar duct-taped back-to-back, blindfolded, and gagged before either dwarf had time to reach for his Glock.

"Time for a little ride," grinned Suttung, "I think we'll use your boat. I see that you have a nice 500-pound mushroom anchor in her that's doing nothing much in particular . . . ."

Well, children, before you knew it, Suttung was "made" and had gotten 100% of the stock in the F&G Distillery. This included the entire inventory, as well as the dwarves' recipes. Fjalar and Galar had apparently gone on an extended vacation "for their health" with no notice, and were never seen again.

Suttung was now a Big Man; unfortunately for him, he was also a blowhard and braggart. Two ravens, who just happened to be in the vicinity, heard about Secret Recipe Mead, and how Suttung's Family business was going to take over the Adult Beverage Wholesale Cooperative as a monopoly. The mayor (Odin) was quite concerned about these developments, so Heimdall put on his black turtleneck with "BATF" in big golden runes on the back, his badge, and his black baseball cap. Heimdall also deputized the local Guildmaster of the Mage's Guild (Odin) as an undercover agent.

Odin was disguised as an unscrupulous grain and honey merchant named Bolverk. He wore Kevlar long johns underneath his

6-SIBL

Levis, and he was wired with a microphone. He also packed an AK-47 disguised as a whetstone (remember, Odin was not only a god, but also a top-bracket wizard). As Bolverk, Odin's assignment was to work his way up through Suttung's organization. Heimdall would handle the frontal attack.

Your Mom made me swear not to tell you any details about the gore-spattered shootouts and senseless violence that came next. It wasn't pretty, children, and it wasn't quick. Eventually Odin suborned a giant named Baugi, who made a living drilling dynamite holes for miners and road construction companies. He got Baugi to drill a 2-inch hole straight through the side of the mountain so's he could slip in a microphone on a snake to get the goods on Suttung. After a few false starts (and some AK-47 psychology), Baugi's drill got through. Odin was about to crack the Big Man's *sanctum sanctorum*.

What Odin/Bolverk heard, though, was the sound of a woman undressing. Again, children, I shall spare your tender ears from the details, but the upshot was that Odin (disguised as the microphone) slipped through the hole, stayed in the *sanctum sanctorum* for three days, and then beat it for home disguised as a catcher for the Baltimore Orioles (it was World Series season, and the Orioles were on top). Suttung came home just as Odin was leaving. The giant did a wheelie with his Cadillac and took off after Odin.

Since he was an Oriole, Odin could fly. Which meant that he put a long high one over the Green Monster. Unfortunately, Suttung's limo had VTOL capability and followed hot on Odin's heels, trying to get a bead on him with a Sidewinder missile. Odin threw out chaff, which saved his skin long enough to get over the Asgard Wall. Heimdall and Tyr had alerted the Army Reserves as well as the FBI. Suttung was *theirs*.

Just as Odin cleared the wall, a warhead detonated almost on top of him, and the contents of 3 barrels of Secret Recipe Mead (which the god had stashed up his sleeve . . . remember, the guy was a magician!) exploded into an alcoholic rain. The BATF agents on the ground, who were also magical, had plenty of time to get every pot and pan in Asgard under the falling drops, and were able to catch almost all of it. Suttung realized that the jig was up, and that he was being targeted by weapons that even he couldn't handle. He beat it out of there, and lived to see another day.

61

Heimdall impounded the mead as evidence, but the town magistrate (Odin) suggested that the local saloon take possession. A compromise was reached that the mead should be stored at the Vanaheim Memorial Library, with small withdrawals allowed when Idunn held one of her poetry slams. Suttung moved back home to Sicily, and things quieted down. But somehow a new line of Panther Sweat, tasting remarkably like that originally manufactured by Fjalar and Galar (remember them?), was suddenly available at The Valhalla Sports Bar and Grill.

And that, children, is how Odin got the goods on Don Guido's grand-nephew, as well as his recipe files. Heimdall has an APB out on him, and he's made the Ten Most Wanted list. The reward for Suttung's capture and conviction, I understand, is in the high six figures.

Chapter 7

THOR'S SUMMER VACATION,
PART ONE.

Hullo, children, I see that it's bedtime again. Did you brush your teeth and wash behind your ears? Yes? Good! OK, snuggle down under the covers, there, and I'll tell you all about Thor's Summer Vacation. It's quite a saga, and it may take me two nights to tell it right.

Once upon a time, Thor was watching a "Cheers" re-run with Odin while Frigg was out bowling with the girls. Odin kept plying the both of them with beer, but even so, Thor was bored. To tell the truth, "Cheers" was a bit highbrow for him; he liked something with a lot more action in it. Like "Walker, Texas Ranger" or "Nash Bridges". Or a good demolition derby. But since Odin was supplying the beer, Thor stayed put and pretended to follow what was going on.

Odin did his best to keep the thunder-god amused, but after about his eighth six-pack, Thor was still restless. Watching other folks drink on the tube wasn't any fun, since they weren't available for a good fist-fight or other interactive sport. Thor sighed deeply as he started in on Odin's last bottle of Sven's Wicked Midsummer Ale. Odin knew that he had to suggest something pretty soon, because there were no more alcoholic beverages in the house, which meant that Thor would get into the Sterno next.

Thor sucked down the last of the suds just as the commercial came on. This featured a few scantily dressed dwarven maidens revving up some monster trucks while a snappily-dressed Jotun with a loud tie and a booming voice proclaimed that there would be a big rally at Utgard-Loki's brand new pool hall on the coming weekend. Seems that Utgard-Loki had done so well with his first joint that he'd gone into franchising, and the Grand Opening of his second establishment was going to feature all sorts of fun. Thor sat up, fascinated, as the large, gaily-painted vehicles roared around a track, leaping piles of smashed monster trucks from previous go-arounds. One truck caught the top of the wreckage and spun to one side, crunching another flat as it came down. Both trucks plus the wreckage burst into flame as the dwarves tried to escape and scamper to safety. One made it to the sidelines without catching fire, while Thor cheered her on.

"Hey, Thor, maybe you oughta go catch the opening," said Odin hopefully. "You'll hafta get an early start, because this new place is quite a long ways from here, and the beer'll go early if the giants get into it."

Thor, cheered by the prospect of more beer and some good fun, was perfectly agreeable. Most of the giants he knew couldn't hold more than a few kegs, and that meant a decent knock-down drag-out no-holds-barred brawl. He patted his hammer, got up, thanked Odin for this wonderful suggestion, and trotted out the door. Odin was left with a biggish mountain of empties, which he and the wolves shoveled into the recycling bin. The ravens supervised from on top of the refrigerator, making the occasional snide comment now and again, and ducking empties. Frigg was big into recycling, and heaven help Odin if he tossed a bottle or can into the regular trash. Fortunately, the mess was pretty much cleaned up by the time she came home, so there was no trouble that night.

The next morning, Thor hopped onto his Harley and roared out of Asgard, shattering the pre-dawn stillness with his tuned mufflers. A few sleepy curses greeted this din, but Thor was out of range before the rain of old shoes, rocks, and flatirons could hit him. Those townsfolk who kept crossbows beside their beds had a better chance, but Thor was on a roll and over the Bifrost Memorial Bridge before the archers could crank their bowstrings back. Crossbows have a lot of punch to them, so it was just lucky for Thor that he was doing 90 as he passed through town.

Heimdall poked his head out of the tollbooth as the thunder god roared past, but he knew better than to yell something nasty. Thor had a quick temper, and was obviously on some kind of mission. It was simply a lot easier on one's health to just go back to bed again and hope to get a few more winks before the morning rush hour.

Thor headed due east, cheerfully humming as he drove. He got lost a few times, since he hadn't caught the address of this new place, and he also didn't like to ask for directions. Actually, he was lost most of the time. But it was good rough terrain, and Thor loved to put his bike through its paces.

He'd been lost for about three hours this latest time when he noticed several things. First, his gas gauge hovered on empty. Second, the sun was beginning to set. Third, he hadn't packed anything, not even food or something to drink or a sleeping bag. Fourth, he didn't have a clue where he was, which way was north, or how to get home. He was in the deep woods, and all he saw were lots and lots of trees and swarms of hungry mosquitos. Fifth, he had also forgotten to pack money . . . but he *did* have his Asgard Express card with him. He never, ever left home without it. When Thor got lost, he did it up brown.

The Harley coughed just as the sun finished setting, coughed again, and sputtered to a halt. Out of gas. Lost. Hungry. Not a good thing. Thor slid off the bike and started pushing it toward a light faintly glimmering off to his right through the trees. He wasn't humming any more as he grimly hauled the heavy machine over fallen logs and through a nice wide bog loaded with bullfrogs and leeches and slimy things that wound around his ankles. Fortunately, he was rewarded by coming out onto a rutted dirt road leading up to a ramshackle series of shacks and huts. The light was coming from the windows of the biggest shack, which also featured a weary red neon sign proclaiming "Ingqvist's A-1 Mini-Mart, Tattoo Parlor, and Garage".

Thor parked the Harley outside the front door. He pounded on the door, which quickly opened. When Thor pounded on a door, he wasn't subtle, and it was clear that if he kept it up, the whole building would collapse. A balding, white-whiskered man wearing greasy overalls welcomed the thunder god in, a bit fearfully perhaps, but courteously. He didn't have a clue who Thor was, but he saw that this particular customer was big, strong, not in the best of moods, and obviously used to getting his own way.

"Kinda late to be out, ain't it?" the old codger asked, "What kin we do fer ya?"

"Need some gas for my bike," Thor answered, "A case of Ding-Dongs and a keg of beer would be nice, too."

"Gas we got, but we're fresh outta food. Delivery comes tomorrow, we hope. Maybe we can scrounge up something if yer not particular."

"You take plastic?" Thor asked hopefully, "It's all I got on me."

"Sure, no sweat! Weasel, MasterSpend, whatever. By the way, I'm Ole Ingqvist, this is my wife Lena, and my kids Thjalfi and Roskva," he continued, pointing out a tallish woman wearing an "Uff, da!" T-shirt, a gangling teenage boy with acne and long wheat-blond hair tied back in a ponytail, and a younger teenage girl with a purple and green Mohawk, pierced eyebrows, and an impressive array of epidermal artwork. Thor's mouth gaped open in surprise at this last vision; he wondered if she was human or something else. Ole, the paterfamilas, noticed Thor's fascination and added, "If ya need a tattoo, Roskva can set you up with a nice one while you wait. Lena, we got any doughnuts left?"

"All we got is this one that fell on the floor, ain't too many dog hairs on it and they can be picked off easy enough. Coffee?"

Thor sat down on a creaking orange Naugahyde stool and accepted a cup of joe which poured and looked like tar. The doughnut came next, served on a paper towel. At this point, Thor wasn't feeling choosy, and he gulped them both down in about one nanosecond flat. It was only when he was licking out the cup that he saw the eyes of the entire family looking sadly at the paper towel.

"Um, that doughnut was supper for all of us," Lena said quietly, "It's all the food we had."

Thor felt awful. He couldn't give the doughnut back, not in any edible condition. He had to think of something to do for this poor family which had welcomed him in, a complete stranger, and offered him all they had. His right hand, still holding the mug, fell down at his side, the china clinking against his hammer as it went past.

His hammer! Mjollnir was magical. Could do lots of things. Hey, maybe . . . maybe it could bring something to life, *create* something instead of always smashing things up. Worth a try. Too hungry to think straight, but this is cockeyed enough that it might work. Thor slowly got up and carefully put the mug on the ancient Formica counter and said "Lena, put a big kettle of water on; I'll be right back."

As the family looked up at him with sudden hope, the thunder god swung around and headed out to his customized Harley, which had real goat's horn handlebars. Raising Mjollnir high in both hands, he called upon the Cosmic Forces to bring the erstwhile owners of aforesaid handlebars back to life for a little while, so that a starving family (and famished thunder god) might have something more than air and dust mites to eat for dinner.

Thunder cracked and rolled, and lightning flashed around the thunder god's high-held hammer. His red hair and beard whipped in a sudden gale as Thor chanted and channeled the Power. Tree branches tossed, and two of the weaker shacks disintegrated into a flurry of weathered timber and debris. The Ingqvists dove for the floor as a tremendous lightning bolt sizzled down straight onto Thor's hammer and thence to the Harley in a terrific flash of blue-white fire. The loudest BOOOM! of thunder that the Ingqvists had ever heard rattled the dishes, panicked the dog, and knocked down another shack. The Mini-Mart etc. still stood, but its timbers creaked alarmingly and some of its roof shingles sailed away like lichen-coated Frisbees.

When the Ingqvists could see and hear again, there was their guest/customer walking through the door with two dead goats slung over his shoulder. If they'd looked past the god, they would have seen that his Harley was no longer parked in front of their store. But their eyes were still dazzled from that last flash and their ears still rang from the noise. Thor sat down heavily, letting the goats slide to the floor. Pulling out a belt-knife, he slit them open along the belly, skinning them very carefully so that the hides were not all hacked up. He then cut the bodies free from the head and legs and tail, and one by one put them into Lena's kettle. Next, the goat hides with attached heads and feet were placed fur-side down on the counter. The Ingqvists, huddled in one corner, watched these proceedings with awed expressions and in total silence.

It was clear that it would take quite a while for that kettle to come to a boil and cook the goats if it sat on that puny little fire. Thor once again pulled out Mjollnir and shoved its head into the greasy water. Once again lightning shimmered around his head, and suddenly the pot was boiling furiously. Thor stood there, motionless except for the lightning, for about five minutes while the Ingqvist family stared numbly. He then pulled his hammer out of the stew, licked it clean, and replaced it in his belt.

"Got any salt and pepper?" the god asked, "Some basil would be nice, too, and maybe a bit of thyme and some onions".

"Guh-guh-guh-guh," said Lena brightly, and "Hoooooolleyyy cowww!" whispered Ole, and "Eeeeewww, the guts are in there, too!" whimpered Roskva, and "Coooooolll!" shouted Thjalfi. Thor emptied the plastic salt and pepper shakers which had been sitting on the counter into the stew, followed by the contents of a half bottle of Tabasco.

"OK, let's EAT!!! But please, please be careful of the bones, especially the tiny ones. Don't chew them at all or cut them in any way, just put them all onto the hides there! Every single bone has to be returned, or the magic will go wrong!" And, thought Thor to himself, if the magic goes wrong, then my Harley can't be reconstituted and then I'll get mad and then this nice family will all be toast.

Needless to say, boiled goat, guts and all, made a wonderful supper. They ate every last scrap, carefully placing the bones onto the hides on the counter. Thor had a lot of explaining to do, what with all the lightning and thunder and magic. The Ingqvists, impressed that one of the mythical Æsir had actually graced their establishment with his presence, got him to sign their guest log, and they gave him the best bed in the place to sleep in.

Before he turned in, Thor carefully wrapped the bones in the hides and went outside with them, cautioning the family not to look at what he was doing. In any case, Thjalfi (whose eye was at a knothole) couldn't see much because it was pitch-dark outside. No lightning this time, just a low murmuring as the god knelt, his broad back to the door. He then rose to his feet and came back inside, exhausted and empty-handed.

"I've got to get on the road first thing in the morning", he said, "Gotta find out where that new pool hall opening party is going on." Thjalfi's eyes glowed as he blurted out "Utgard-Loki's Pool Palace Number Two? Coool!" His folks wouldn't let him go to the Grand Opening because he was only a teenager and he might get into trouble.

The next morning, Thor awoke feeling quite rested and fed. He rolled out of bed and quietly went outside. Sure enough, there was his Harley, complete with its horn handlebars and without a scratch on it. Breathing a sigh of relief, he wheeled it up to one of the gas pumps and filled the tank. He saw an empty jerry can inside the garage, which he filled with gas and strapped to the back of the bike. All he had to do was to go thank the Ingqvists for their hospitality, pay for the gas, and be off.

The Ingqvists all stood in front of the Mini Mart etc. to wave goodbye. Thor kicked the starter, and the bike's motor roared into life. He slipped the brake . . . and went nowhere. He gunned it, but the bike just sat there. The motor sounded fine, but the wheels weren't turning. Thor hopped off again and started to study the situation. Being attuned to that bike, it didn't take him long to discover that the clutch was kaput. Like, it didn't engage. Thor looked up at the Ingqvists with a puzzled expression, and then at Thjalfi with an intense expression.

"Hey, you! C'mere!" growled the thunder god. Thjalfi suddenly began to look a bit pale and twitchy as the god continued, "Did . . . you . . . damage . . . any . . . of . . . those . . . bones . . . last . . . night???"

"Uuuh, I mighta. I guess maybe I fergot what you said . . . " Thjalfi confessed slowly, "I hadn't eaten in two days and I was so hungry and I'm sorry that I dug the marrow outa that leg-bone and I won't do it ever ever ever again . . . " his voice trailed off uncertainly. Then the boy's eyes brightened. "Hey, I can fix it for you, I got parts and I've been fixing stuff for Pop in the garage, and I can fix just about anything with wheels!"

Thor looked over at Ole, who was trying hard not to shake in his boots. Ole just nodded weakly at Thor, agreeing with Thjalfi's claims. Thor looked back at Thjalfi and said, "OK, you got an hour. If you can fix it in one hour or less, I'll forgive you . . . on the one condition that you come with me on this little trip with your tools, in case it breaks down again!"

It took 59 minutes 37 seconds, but the job got done. Thjalfi really *was* a genius with motor vehicles, and he had that bike ready to go just in time. He was also spurred on by the prospect of getting to go to the big party without his folks butting in and telling him to stay home and be good. He packed a few things and was just about to hop on the bike behind Thor when Lena shouted out "STOP! I'm sending your little sister along to chaperone you; you won't dare get into trouble if she's around! Roskva, dear, pack your tattooing kit; maybe you can make some extra money while you're there!"

And so the three of them roared off. Fortunately, Thjalfi knew *exactly* where Utgard-Loki's new establishment was, so Thor didn't get lost again.

Kids, I promised your Mom that I wouldn't keep you up late on a school night. There's a lot more of this story left, too much for one night. I'll tell you the rest of it tomorrow night, and I'll leave in the gory parts if you're really, really good in school.

Chapter 8

THOR'S SUMMER VACATION,
PART TWO.

My, you kids sure got into bed *quickly* tonight! Are you all ready for the rest of the story about Thor's summer vacation? Hey! I'm not deaf! I can *hear* you!

OK, we left off where Thor was riding his Harley to the Grand Opening of Utgard Loki's Pool Hall Number Two. Seated behind him were Thjalfi and Roskva, two humans who he'd accumulated along the way. They had a fine ride that day, even with three on the Hog. Thor found an abandoned sand pit which made for some great dirt-bike maneuvers. Then there was the quarry, a power line right-of way, some water, and a few logging roads. They got lunch at a Midgard Fried Ptarmigan, as well as a "to go" Banquet For Twenty-Four.

As the sun was setting, they came to a large cave near a brook and decided to camp there for the night. Thor had taken the precaution of doing a little back-door trading with the manager of the

Midgard Fried Ptarmigan, so he had a gallon jug of white lightning
to liven things up that evening. Thor, seeing that this was a pretty
large cave which had side-rooms, parked his bike in one side-
room and claimed its neighbor for his bedroom. Roskva laid out
soft pine branches in three of the side-rooms for bedding, Thjalfi
chopped firewood for a nice campfire, and Thor started in on the
bug juice. They had a companionable meal, disrupted only when
Loki came out of the woods just as they'd gotten the food out.

Loki, it turned out, was looking for new financial opportuni-
ties. The bouncers at the original Pool Hall all knew him by sight
now, which made things a bit difficult. This new establishment
should bring a whole slew of total strangers, suckers ripe for the
plucking.

Thor grudgingly offered Loki a wing and a snort. Loki thanked Thor, ate the wing (bones and all), passed on the tonsil wash, and reached for another piece of crispy fried ptarmigan. Thor got there first, so Loki had to be content with what he'd gotten. Roskva made up a pine-branch bed for Loki in the last side-room of the cave while Thor concentrated on finishing the contents of his jug and discussing the finer points of his Harley with Thjalfi.

That night at about midnight, they awoke to a loud crashing in the woods outside and about a 7.3 Richter scale shaking of their temporary abode. There was a horrible grinding, drawn out howl coming out of the woods near the cave. Thor grabbed his hammer and roared out to do battle if such was in the offing. He couldn't see anything in the dark, so he threw his hammer at where he thought the loudest noise was coming from. The noises stopped abruptly, after which Mjollnir came winging out of the woods to smack back in Thor's hand.

The racket started up again about ten minutes later, and kept up off and on throughout most of the night. Thor had to get up a few more times and deal with it. The last time he did so was at about 5:30 in the morning, when the sky was just beginning to lighten and he could see a bit better. He followed the sounds to a clearing, where he found a huge Jotun lying on the ground on his back, mouth open, and snoring. It was Skrymir, the head bouncer at Utgard-Loki's Pool Hall Number One, and this was where that horrific noise was coming from. It was also very, very obvious that Skrymir suffered from really bad sleep apnea, as well as enlarged tonsils and adenoids.

Imagine the *worst* snoring you've ever heard, multiply it by three, and then make it six times as loud. Thor grabbed Mjollnir and hit the giant as hard as he could on the head, right where the noise was coming from. Skrymir snorted, stopped snoring, blinked, rubbed his eyes, and sleepily turned over onto his left side. The snoring started up again within ten seconds. Thor swung Mjollnir again, even harder, at Skrymir's beak of a nose. This got the giant to look blearily at Thor, grunt, scratch his armpit, and roll over on his other side . The third time, Skrymir shook himself like a large wet dog and then climbed sleepily to his feet. As the Jotun wandered off, Thor returned to the cave. Not even a bird chirped, so maybe Thor could catch a few Z's before the alarm clock rang.

Needless to say, nobody had gotten much sleep that night, and Thor was in a filthy mood when the sun finally rose and it was time to hit the road again. When the thunder god pushed his bike out of the cave, all he saw was a picturesque-looking human male standing in the small clearing, quietly holding a small black cylinder to one eye and looking around at the scenery. The stranger had a salt-and-pepper beard and hair, wore a white turtleneck, and carried a clipboard upon which he was making notes between observations. In the distance, there was a crashing, crunching, splintering, crackling, booming noise, which came closer and closer to them.

"Hey!" shouted the thunder god, "What'n blazes is going on here? Where's the fight?"

Thor was all set for a nice morning workout and sparring practice, but the noises ceased abruptly as the stranger turned to face him. A broad grin split the human's face as he approached the thunder god, hand outstretched in greeting.

"Oh, that's in the can now, the light's no longer good," said the man cryptically, "They're getting ready to shoot the next scene." He swivelled around to shout "Quiet on the set!" at the woods in back of him, and then screamed "Four, three, two, one . . . roll 'em!"

By now, the others had joined Thor in front of the cave. The stranger darted off to one side as Skrymir came out of the woods towards them, big as life, well bigger than life . . . heck, a *lot* bigger than life, chuckling deep in his chest and reaching out with one large meaty hand toward the thunder god. Thor had Mjollnir out and cocked for action in no time, but the Jotun merely laughed again, looked beyond the god, and said "Thank you for finding my driving glove, fella! Wondered where I'd dropped it!"

Ignoring a whirring noise which came from the woods, Thor wheeled around to see that the cave had shrunk to the size of a Jotun glove . . . why, it *was* a Jotun glove! Thor, Loki, Thjalfi, and Roskva looked at each other, puzzled, and then back at the Jotun, who was now normal-sized for a giant. "Musta been the kerosene in that hooch last night", Thor thought to himself. Loki smirked and the two humans merely looked confused. Skrymir reached over, picked up his glove, shook it out, and put it on with a happy sigh.

"CUT! PRINT!" That human had quite a set of pipes, yah shure! Beaming, he walked up to the giant and slapped him on the back of his knee. Remember, Skrymir *was* a giant.

"Hey, Thor, meet my technical director, Staffan Spelbjerg! Staff, this is the one and only Thor, the fella I was telling you about. Great action hero potential, don't you think?" Skrymir was clearly enjoying himself at Thor's expense, which Thor didn't take too kindly, especially from a Jotun. Ignoring the snickering Loki and the giant, the thunder god shook the human's hand politely enough, and then he asked about the grand opening of Pool Hall Number Two.

"Yah, we're just on our way there, ain't we, Staff? Your crew all set up for the day's shoot?" Skrymir sure wasn't making much

81

sense to Thor, who had come to the conclusion that the giant and the human had begun celebrating early. He hoped that there'd be some beer left . . . and if the party'd already begun, maybe there wouldn't be any beer left.

Staffan suggested that they all hurry, as the light would be just right in about a half an hour. The logging road they'd been on suddenly turned to pavement, with neatly-trimmed shrubs along the side. When they came around the last curve, Thor stopped his bike and stared at the large emporium which stood upon about three acres of golf-green grass. It looked like a wedding cake designed by Ludwig the Mad. A huge sign proclaimed "Utgard-Loki's Famous Pool Hall Number Two" in six-foot tall flashing neon runes, with running arrows indicating the entrance. That latter feature was clearly identifiable without the sign; its heavy bronze doors were flung wide open by a pair of ogres, and the sound of music floated on the air.

Well, OK, maybe the music didn't float. Jotun bands don't play floating music. This stuff more sorta stomped heavy-footed, occasionally stumbling hard or losing its way. But it *was* loud and had kind of a catchy rhythm. A gaudily-uniformed Jotun came up to them, saying that he was the valet parker, and that he'd take good care of the bike. Thor was suspicious, but Skrymir said that he'd parked a lot of vehicles and hadn't wrinkled one yet. The "yet" part bothered the thunder god, but his attention was distracted by the sound of raucous laughter, some crunching and crashing sounds, a siren beginning to wail, and the band enthusiastically starting in on a new selection. It was Party Time.

This place was a lot bigger on the inside than it appeared on the outside. Slot machines lined the walls, and uniformed Jotuns shuttled back and forth with kegs, sacks of change, fresh decks of cards, and trays of hors d'oeuvres. Thor was content; Jotun hors d'oeuvres tended towards whole roasted oxen, boars, pigs, and Cajun-style blackened whole sheep. Chips and Cheese Noodles were piled high in dumpsters, and kegs of just about every kind of beer imaginable were all over the place. Thor rubbed his hands together and grabbed a full tray from the nearest Jotun. He then sat on a closeby keg, which he had quickly emptied before coming to rest. Loki had disappeared, and Thjalfi and Roskva just stood there, gawking at everything around them in wide-eyed wonder.

"Time for the floor show!" announced Skrymir. That Spelbjerg fellow had vanished, but the kegs hadn't, so Thor grabbed a few and followed the Jotun into the depths of the hall. The din was almost unbearably loud, what with the band and the drunken giants whooping it up, and the troll girls who were exotic dancers bumping and grinding. Bumping and grinding, to a troll, meant just that. If you weren't careful, you'd get a stone-hard trollish elbow in your side or back, or get mashed and ground against a wall. It was just the type of party that Thor was up for, and he happily joined in the fun.

Utgard-Loki himself was lounging in a humongous throne-like reclining chair at one end of the hall. As Thor, Thjalfi, and Roskva came in, the giant signaled for the next act to begin. The lights dimmed, and the drummer hit a ragged roll on a kettledrum. A baby-blue spotlight came on, wandered around the room, and settled on Loki, who jumped guiltily away from one of the roulette wheels.

"Har, har, har!" laughed Utgard-Loki merrily, "Little Loki wants to play, eh? Hey, pipsqueak, whatcha want to do? You gotta choice of swimming through that tank of piranha after taking a bath in some blood I got handy, or you can see if you can walk that tightrope, er, tight-snake that I got strung up there near the roof, or ya can try yer hand at out-eating Logi, my little nephew, here."

Loki looked at the swarm of hungry piranha, which were looking beadily and hopefully back at him. He then looked up at the snake, which drooled poison and twitched uncomfortably; it obviously didn't like being stretched out like that. Lastly, he looked at Logi, a scrawny nerdy little weedy type with flame-red hair, far too many teeth, and an eager expression.

Now, eating was one of Loki's favorite things. Oh, money was right up there, too, along with cheating at cards, practical jokes, and sassing various members of the Æsir Establishment. The first two choices looked as if they wanted to eat him, so the third seemed to be his best shot.

"I'll go for the eating contest", proclaimed Loki, looking at the little fellow who was to be his competition. He couldn't hold much, maybe a gallon on the outside, thought Loki, good odds there. Maybe I'll put down a side-bet here and there . . . these chuckleheads haven't seen me in action!

A cafeteria table was brought out, piled high with food. Forty-pound stuffed turkeys, four hundred-pound stuffed hippopotami, vats of biscuits and gravy, mountains of mashed potatoes, acres of cornbread, and in the middle, right on top, was one Jotun-style watermelon split in half a 55-gallon drum. Loki and Logi took their places at the opposite ends of the table, Utgard-Loki fired a shot from his .45 Magnum, and the racers took off.

Kids, Loki was a really fast eater, sorta reminds me of your uncle Kjell back when he was on the high school football team. Kjell could empty a 'fridge in less than half an hour, but Loki had him beat. His whole top half was a blur, and the table top in front of him emptied rapidly. Loki didn't use any forks or knives, or even good table manners. He packed that food away almost faster'n he could swallow. But when he got to the watermelon split, there was Logi sitting in the dish, licking up the last of it. And then the table fell over, scattering plates and bones all over the place. Turns out that Logi had eaten his half of the table, too, even the steel legs. Loki had left his table half, as well as the crockery and bones . . . and Logi had won! The Jotuns cheered and clapped as Loki staggered off to the side of the room, desperately looking for some Alka-Seltzer.

The spotlight then swivelled over to Thjalfi. Utgard-Loki offered him the same first two choices as Loki got, or to run a race against the local track star, Hugi. Needless to say, Thjalfi was almost as good at running as he was at fixing Harleys, so he picked that one. Hugi came out, a gangly, lean kid in a baggy runner's suit with the number 8 on the front and back of the tank top. Utgard-Loki waved his right hand, and suddenly there was a running track right there in the hall. Reminds me of the holodeck on "Star Trek", the way that track just appeared. Thjalfi stripped to his BVD's and the two runners took their places at the starting blocks. Once more Utgard-Loki's .45 Magnum spoke, and they were off!

Kids, it turned out that Thjalfi could almost outrun the wind. He could certainly leave a cheetah in the dust. But it was Hugi who left Thjalfi in the dust; when he hit his stride, that "8" flipped over into the infinity sign. Hugi broke the tape while Thjalfi was still in the backstretch. Utgard-Loki and the other Jotuns roared with laughter, and Loki firmly and ruefully resolved to stop betting for a while. Thjalfi managed to make it to the finish line, but he keeled over after that and several dwarven girls hauled him off to one side as he gasped for breath and twitched faintly.

The spotlight then steadied on Thor. The god eyed the fish and the snake, which made them nervous. The fish all crowded to the far side of the tank, trying to hide. The snake managed to wiggle itself free and took off for parts unknown as fast as it could move. This left only the god standing there, blinking in the light.

"Hey, Thor, ten smackeroos says you can't empty this drinking horn fulla Old Iron-Guts Lager in three gulps!" called out the giant, "You on?"

"Yah, shure!" grinned the thunder god, "I've got a wicked thirst, and I betcha I could empty any horn you had in one gulp! Bring it on!"

So Utgard-Loki passed Thor a big drinking horn, one of the really long kinds that come from those extinct European bulls, dripping foam. The god took a deep breath, put the horn to his lips, and started chugging.

Now, you know that Thor could really suck down the suds. I don't even think he swallowed; he just poured and poured and poured. After about six minutes, he came up for air and looked inside the horn. To his surprise, the liquid had only gone down about a half an inch. The god hyperventilated and then tried again.

Have you ever seen a fraternity chugging contest? Oh, yeah, you're too young for that kind of stuff . . . what, you *did*? Do your folks know about that? If they find out, your uncle Kjell is going to be in serious trouble, even if he *did* win. Well, anyway, Thor took twice as long and drank twice as much this second time. When he lowered the horn, he gasped for air and it took a little time for him to catch his breath. The beer was only about an inch and a half down, which meant that Thor had to kill the rest in the last shot. He burped thoughtfully, buuuurped again, breathed deeply, and set the horn to his lips for the third and final time.

It was sort of like the sound that Niagra Falls makes, the sound that was produced by that beer pouring into the thunder god's throat. This was a championship chug. Your uncle Kjell couldn't come *near* to this, even though he *is* the Alpha-Delta-Phi champion and holds the Golden Pretzel Award. When Thor finally gave up, the horn was still more than three-quarters full. Thor had lost, which meant that a small horde of uniformed Jotuns carrying moneybags shuttled back and forth between the onlookers as bets were paid off. The thunder god buuuuuhuuuurped once again, and sat down suddenly on a bench. He wasn't used to having the beer outlast him.

"Hey!" suddenly shouted Utgard-Loki, "Someone get that damned cat outta here! The lady who owns him has a mean right jab with her nålbinding needle, and she doesn't like it at all when Magnus comes over here! Thor, ya wanna toss him out the back door?"

Thor looked blearily over at the cat, who stood proudly in the spotlight, his tail waving gently in the air. In case you wanted to know, kids, this was Ch. Freyzoo's Magnus the Bold, a skogkatt . . . oh, that's a Norwegian Forest Cat . . . with impeccable credentials and an impressive, gleaming white bib of fur on his chest. He had the spotlight, it was showtime, and he wasn't about to leave.

Thor heaved himself to his feet and walked soggily over to Magnus, who looked up at the god with a bored expression. Thor stooped and put his hands under the cat's belly to pick him up. Magnus obligingly bent in the middle as the god lifted his hands, but it was if his four huge, furry paws were epoxied to the floor. You kids know how cats can play with gravity? If a cat doesn't want to be picked up, he magically seems to find extra pounds somewhere, and he gets very heavy, especially if he's sleeping on your bladder in the morning. Well, Magnus didn't seem to want to be moved from His Spot, and did the same kind of gravity tricks.

Now, Thor was the weight-lifting champion of Thrudheim
Athletic Club, and he wasn't going to let some pampered tomcat
with an attitude make him look silly. With a grunt and a heave, he
lifted and lifted . . . and the cat somehow managed to arch himself
so's his feet were still on the floor, even though his bellybutton
was some two feet or more above the top of Thor's head. The
thunder god summoned his chi, screamed some incomprehen-
sible syllable, and lifted as high as he could, standing on tiptoes.
Magnus twitched, and one broad front paw was finally raised
about half an inch off the floor. Thor, who couldn't lift any higher,
dropped his load (seemed as if that cat weighed a coupla tons! he
thought to himself, I'd sure *hate* to have him jump on me!). Magnus
looked up at the thunder god disdainfully, twitched his ears, flicked
his tail, and strolllled off slowly towards the kitchen. The Jotuns
were rolling with laughter, slapping their thighs and gasping for
breath between guffaws, and Thor felt like last week's breakfast.

When Utgard-Loki was finally able to get the laughter-tears
out of his eyes and the laughter-crick out of his stomach, he pointed
to the thunder god and started laughing all over again.

"C-c-couldn't even put out the CAT!!! Bwwaaa-haa-HAAA-
HAAAAR!!!!", and that set the rest of the Jotuns off, which was
just about to set Thor off. But just in time, Utgard-Loki calmed
down enough to say, "Hey, I got someone you can rassle, someone to take yer grudge out on!"

Thor was ready for a rassle. He had built up a good head of
steam, and was soooo ready to pound something flat. The giant
waved, and the baby spot flashed across the floor to a little old
lady who was slowly getting up from her seat near a blackjack
table. She musta been a hundred and twenty years old! Her face
was like a prune, and she was all sorta hunched over and walked
carefully as if she was afraid that just moving might break something. She had on some sort of white pants suit with a black sash

around her waist, and her walker was decorated with white and black ribbons.

Thor eyed the ancient matriarch with disbelief. He was supposed to hit an old lady??? OK, maybe he wasn't a Boy Scout, and sure, he'd roughed up the female side on occasion, but that was because those females were ogresses or giants or trolls who had wanted to wipe the floor with Thor, dead or barely alive. If a female started the fight, Thor would be perfectly happy to end it. But this grandmotherly little old lady looked as if she'd fall apart if you so much as *looked* at her funny.

The giants were having a grand time. The betting was running heavily against Thor . . . Loki had decided to break his vow of abstinence and put all he had on the little old lady. Had a hard time finding takers, too. Thor was *not* amused.

"Annnnd in the right corrrnerrr dressed in whiiite, we have Elli! Annnd in the left corrnerrr dressed in red, brown, black, green, yellow, and blue, we have Thorrrr!" boomed a loudspeaker, followed by a loud "CLANNNGGG!" and then the little old lady threw the walker back over her head, hunkered down, and spread her arms out to her sides in sort of a waiting posture. Thor imitated the arms bit and grunted out a quick apology to his adversary. One gentle backhand oughta do it; sweep her into the crowd of Jotuns who would catch her before she hit the floor.

Thor swung easily . . . and when the stars stopped flashing, he was flat on his back about twelve feet behind the little old lady, who was carefully edging around to face him.

"Whoa, little old ladies aren't *supposed* to throw thunder gods around like that!" growled Thor, as he surged to his feet and charged at the little old lady. Wham! Thor got another astronomy lesson, and the giants fell off their chairs, laughing so hard that they cried. Thor decided to take it slowly this time, and circled in cautiously. Elli somehow managed to keep facing him, and when Thor reached in to grab her arms, somehow he suddenly found himself in the wrestling match of his life. No holds barred, and to heck with Queensberry!

That little old lady was some tough, yah shure! Thor wasn't a wimp, but this time he was being outclassed, out-pointed, out-fought, and out-done. It took that little old great-grandmotherly lady only about three minutes to get the thunder god to fall heavily onto one knee . . . he managed to keep himself clear of the mat otherwise . . . and he realized that he was just about to be flattened. He hit the mat with one hand as his sensai had taught him, and the little old lady immediately disentangled herself, backed off, bowed, and reclaimed her walker. Thor, breathing heavily, nodded his head in return, slowly pushing himself to his feet. The giants were almost paralyzed, they were laughing so hard. Loki merely smiled gently as he counted his newfound wealth.

At that point, Thor decided that he'd had just about all the fun he could take, so he sneaked over into a corner, wrapped himself in a hastily-liberated tablecloth, and decided to sleep off all the beer and humility he'd had that evening. Roskva finished up the last tattoo of the evening, something with a flaming skull and barbed wire and snakes, and repacked her gear. Like Loki, she'd also shown a pretty good profit for the evening. Thjalfi had gone out to sleep next to Thor's Hog so that nothing would happen to it during the night.

The next morning, when everybody was sort of awake, the breakfast buffet was served. Shrimp and champagne, scrambled eggs, coffee, lutefisk omelet, the works. That funny fellow Staffan Spelbjerg was back again, looking very pleased with the world. Thor still felt really embarrassed about yesterday's events, and decided to get on the road quickly before anything else humiliated him. So he walked outside with Roskva, Staffan, Loki, and Utgard-Loki as Thjalfi brought the Harley up to the main entrance.

"Good beer'" said Thor sincerely . . . he couldn't say "thank you for the nice party" and mean it. "My pleasure," said the giant, and then as Spelbjerg nudged him, continued, "Oh, I hope you don't mind if we ask you to sign this acting contract and release I got here?"

"Uhhh . . . whaaa?"

"Sorry to do this, fella, but I'd gotten this movie deal that was too good to lose out on. This whole thing was a bunch of special effects for a new fantasy-action thriller that Spelbjerg here is putting together . . . he wanted a top action hero, and you walked right into it. We can offer you two percent of the gross."

"Ummm . . . er . . . ." (Thor didn't want to admit that he hadn't a clue what an action thriller was, or what two percent of the gross meant) . . . "uhhhhh . . . ."

"Look, Thor, it's sort of like 'Candid Camera'. We set up situations and filmed you as you reacted. Remember when you bashed Skrymir three times to stop his snoring? If ya look over there at that mountain, those three deep rocky valleys weren't in it yesterday. That glove-cave was actually a computer animation effect by Paxir . . . those elves can sure whip up some amazing magic! . . ."

"You mean my aim was so bad that I hit a mountain and not a giant at point-blank range?"

"Look for yourself! And Loki there, he was trying to beat out a wildfire, like the ones out in western Midgard. Didn't have a chance. Thjalfi, he tried to race my thoughts, and even I can think faster'n a human can run!"

"Hey, what about me last night?" Thor was beginning to get the idea, and his right hand slowly reached for his hammer. He didn't like being made a fool of, not at all.

"Oh, that drinking horn was magic; its far end was actually deep in the Great Salty Sea . . . you drank so much that there was a really low tide, and it scared the pants off us! We were afraid you'd drink the sea dry! The neighbor's cat was actually the Midgard serpent . . . you came close to pulling its tail out of its mouth, and if that happened, the whole world woulda gotten unzipped. Then, that little old lady? She was really Old Age; you

93

nearly threw *her* once or twice. You ain't mad at me, are ya?" That last was said rather quickly, because Thor was swinging his hammer around his head and calling up the lightning. Loki and all the humans raced off to find some kind of hole to hide in. There was a whirring in the air . . . actually, two whirrings in the air, and then a simultaneous "CUT! PRINT! THAT'S A WRAP!" and "KABOOM!!!!!!" as the hammer struck right in the middle of where Utgard-Loki's solar plexus should be.

When the smoke cleared, Thor, Thjalfi, Roskva, Loki, and the Harley found themselves standing alone in a small clearing, with forest all around them. No castle, no giants, no crazy humans who spoke in tongues, and no road. Nothing to hit. Loki quickly checked his pockets . . . he'd won a coupla thou betting on the old lady . . . and the cash was missing, too. Thor grumped and grumbled under his breath, but there was nothing he could get back at. All they could do was to saddle up again and head back to Asgard via the Ingqvist's. Thor made everybody promise cross their hearts to never, ever breathe a *word* about what went on, and to just say that they were out in the boonies riding the Harley. That lasted only until Staffan Spelbjerg's latest action-thriller movie came out. "Lethal Games" hit the top of the charts and everyone was asking Thor and Loki for their autographs.

But you'd better believe it, children, that the next time Thor saw Utgard-Loki, he and Mjollnir would want to have a little discussion with him. Loki was annoyed, too. Now *everybody* knew what he looked like, which put a serious crimp in his . . . er, creative financial acquisition career.

I'm sorry that there wasn't much bloodshed in this story, but nobody picked the piranha tank. And now it's time to go to sleep . . . and I certainly hope that you're better behaved in school tomorrow! I *heard* what you did to the substitute teacher this morning . . . if you want another story tomorrow night, you'd better shape up fast!

Chapter 9

THOR'S FISHING TRIP

I hear that Daddy's going to take you children fishing to-morrow. What fun! That reminds me of a story about Thor and *his* fishing trip. Would you like to hear it? Yes? OK, here goes.

One beautiful spring day, Thor was idly flipping through a dog-eared copy of "Field and Stream" at the Thrudheim Athletic Club. It was kind of a lazy day, and nothing much was going on at the Club. No action at the Valhalla, either. Jotunheim was quiet, too. Thor was bored out of his skull. He wanted some *action*!

An article caught his eye, the one about looking for the Loch Ness Monster. A few tantalizing pictures accompanied it, but the article concluded that this critter didn't actually exist.

"Ha!" he snorted, "Those guys don't have a *clue* what's out there in the deepwater ocean! *I* know where to find an even *bigger* sea monster!"

That got Thor to thinking. Action. Sea monster. I'm bored. Need action.

The penny dropped. Thor leaped to his feet and ran to the closet where he kept his fishing tackle. The box was small, as he usually used either a grenade or his hammer for fishing. The one reel of line was 2-pound test, which would barely hold an Asgardian minnow. Three rusty #4 fish hooks and a half bottle of Old Raven were the only other things in the box. Obviously Thor hadn't done much fishing in his life, but now was just as good a time as any to correct that situation.

His next step was to hop on the Hog and roar on down to Njord's shack on the docks. Njord knew lots about fishing, and he sold all sorts of fishing tackle and stuff. As he rode, Thor began to grin, and then to smile, and then to laugh. This wasn't going to be such a boring day, after all! When he got there, he was greeted by a world-shaking stale fish smell, a zillion sea gulls, and Njord in that order. Njord had just finished making a huge kettle of clam chowder, and he ladled out a big bowlful for Thor. They sat down on a couple of crates on the dock, sipping the boiling-hot chowder and talking about the latest goings-on in Jotunheim. Njord discreetly avoided mentioning Thor's almost-wedding as "Freyja", which meant that Thor didn't show Njord just how Mjollnir took care of an unpleasant situation.

They also discussed fishing, which was Njord's favorite subject (besides money, that is). Thor outlined his needs, and it turned out that Njord had just what Thor wanted. One of the Jotuns, Hymir by name, owned the excursion fishing smack "My Boat!", and he could supply rental tackle for all occasions. For a slight extra fee he'd throw in a couple of coolers of iced beer, bait, and ham-and-cheese on rye sandwiches. One phone call later, Njord announced that Hymir would be alongside the dock in fifteen minutes. Business had been slow for him, too.

"My Boat!" was about fifty feet long and had twin screws. It had also obviously been a very, very long time since any maintenance had been done on her topsides or the rest of her, for that matter. She also smelled even worse than Njord's docks, if that was possible. Thor parked his Harley in one of Njord's sheds, and hopped aboard. As the boat pulled away from the dock, Thor cracked open his first brewski of the day.

"What'cher after?" asked Hymir in a ripe Bronx accent, "Bottom fish, bluefish, striped bass, shark, cod, mermaids, whatever?"

"I'm after some really *big* game," said Thor, "I'm not in the mood to mess around with small fry!"

"Awright, great white shark OK?"

"Nope, something *much* bigger and meaner than that!" Thor didn't want to say what he actually intended to catch, because he was afraid that Hymir might cancel the charter on the spot and that Thor would find himself back on Njord's dock, bored out of his skull. "I need some serious bait, a tungsten-steel meat-hook, and about a mile of 100,000-ton test line."

"Haw, haw, haw!" roared Hymir, "This I gotta see!" He wiped laughter-tears off his stubbled cheeks and then brought out the line and hook.

"I ain't got no bait that big'" he said, "We gotta stop off at my place an' find somethin' you can use."

"Fine by me'" said the thunder-god lightly, "After all, *I'm* paying, and I want to have some *action!*"

So they motored on over to Bloodlust Harbor in Jotunheim where Hymir kept his boat. After docking, Hymir and Thor headed over towards the giant's bait shack. Now, Hymir had every kind of bait imaginable. Everything from nightcrawlers on up to dead octopus. Octopi. Whatever. Why, he even had mermaid bait! What's that? Oh, mermaids like sweet bread with lots of honey slathered all over it. And you don't use a hook to catch them, just a really good line. What kind of line? Next time you see Frey, ask him; he's got hundreds of 'em!

Well, Thor sifted through everything in that shack and couldn't find what he wanted, bait-wise. So he asked Hymir if he could buy one of his cattle; one of those beauties should make a tempting tidbit for his quarry. Hymir quoted a (for him) reasonable price, and Thor paid up. Thor also had to buy a tankful of gas, since Hymir had conveniently neglected to fill up before collecting his passenger.

While Hymir was tanking up, Thor strode over to Hymir's closest pasture and looked the herd over. There! A huge black bull looked up, pawed the earth, and made for Thor. The fact that Thor had a bright red beard and hair may have had something to do with the single-mindedness of the bull's attention. The bull picked up speed, somewhat like one of those old steam locomotives, with the clear intent of tossing Thor high in the air before trampling him into the dirt. Thor just grinned, gripped his hammer tight, and met the bull head-on. Actually, Mjollnir met the bull head-on. And Thor had his bait.

Thor easily swung the carcass over one shoulder and trotted back to "My Boat!". Hymir looked up, and then started to use some rather ungentlemanly words. It seems that Thor had picked Hymir's prize stud bull, and Hymir was not at all pleased. Especially since the price he'd quoted had been for an old cow. Thor just grinned, slung the animal aboard, and popped open another beer. It was time for some action!

Well, children, what was done was done, and Hymir had to be content with that. "My Boat!" chugged out into the channel and made for the open sea. After about a half hour, Hymir indicated that they'd come to a good fishing spot. Thor just wiped some suds off his mustache and said, "No, let's go farther out! There's nothing here that I'm interested in!"

So Hymir kept heading out farther from shore. Soon they were almost out of sight of land.

"Here we go!", the giant grunted, "There's gotta be some big fish somewhere out here!"

"Let's go out a little farther," suggested the thunder-god, "I'm after a *big* one today!"

Hymir protested that they were getting close to some dangerous waters, and that they might be attacked by sea monsters. Thor just grinned wider, sucked down another brew, and pointed towards the far horizon. Hymir noticed Thor's left hand start to creep toward the handle of his hammer, so he revved up the motors and kept on going away from land.

"This looks like a good spot!" Thor finally said, "I'll bait the hook and you get out the sandwiches!"

So Thor baited his hook with the bull's head and tossed it over the side. He paid out about a quarter of a mile of line and sat back, one hand jigging the line and the other rummaging around for sandwich after sandwich, with a few beers here and there to wet things down. Hymir was looking a bit nervous, but he didn't say anything because Mjollnir was very handy, and he knew that Thor had a quick temper.

About an hour passed, and less than half a case of beer remained. Thor was leaning back in his sport-fisherman's fighting chair with both feet propped up on the gunwhale, placidly moving the tip of his deep-sea rod in lazy figure-eights. Suddenly the tip jerked down violently, and line began to whizzzzzzzz off the reel. When about half a mile of line had paid out, Thor braced himself and yanked hard to set the hook solidly. "My Boat!" immediately started surfing backwards after the submerged whatever-it-was-that-took-the-bait so fast that it threw up rooster tails. Hymir started to scream about sea serpents, but Thor only laughed and began to reel in the line.

You children may have heard about the "Nantucket Sleigh Ride", back when people harpooned whales. "My Boat" was on a stepped-up version of the "Nantucket Sleigh Ride". Whatever was on the end of Thor's line not only pulled the boat backward through the water at speeds varying from 20 to 90 knots, but it also tried jerking the boat side-to-side. Hymir, grabbing the wheel tightly in both hands, could do nothing. The fact that he was thoroughly seasick didn't help. Thor's hair and beard flew in the spray-laden wind, and the thunder-god was laughing maniacally as he cranked even faster on the reel.

It took about two hours before Thor finally got the monster hauled in close to the ship's side. As the thunder-god lifted the rod high so's to pull his quarry out of the water, Hymir got a bleary look at what Thor had caught. There, chewing on the bull's head, was the big, ugly, toothy, tentacle-y, and very, *very* angry head of the most humongous sea monster imaginable. The slitted pupils of its malevolent red-rimmed yellow eyes fixed themselves on Thor. Thor just grinned back and got ready to land his catch.

"Ohhh (bleep!)'" groaned the giant, "That's Jormungandr, the Midgard Serpent! Ain't no *way* we have room on board for even his head, much less the rest of him! And why the (Jotun words designed to strip paint) is it *me* that's at ground zero??!!??"

101

Hymir grabbed the fire axe and desperately chopped at the line where it crossed the gunwhale just as Thor exerted his full strength in an attempt to heave his catch aboard. So violent was that heave that Thor's left foot crunched through the floorboards, bilge space, and bottom of "My Boat!". The axe blade struck true (a miracle!), and the line parted with a twang, whipping back and shearing off part of "My Boat!"'s cabin. Jormungandr, who'd been pulling against the hook, sank back into the water with such violence that the resulting tsunami picked up "My Boat!" and carried it some 50 miles farther out to sea.

Thor was *not* amused. Fortunately there were no sea gulls around to hear what he said to Hymir, but I can guarantee you that the thunder-god peeled every last scrap of paint off the boat, which was rapidly sinking under them. Hymir, meanwhile, had gone past abject terror into a kind of fey utter calm.

"We're dead," said the giant evenly, "We're dead. We're dead. We're dead. We're dead . . . ."

"Wrong! *You're* dead! *You're* dead! *You're* dead!" Thor screamed as he swung Mjollnir at the Jotun. The thunder-god then shook the boat off his foot and set off back towards land. Being a god, he could walk on water just fine. Of course, now he was stomping on water.

56-SIBL

It was almost twilight when Thor got back to Njord's dock. Njord had seen him coming, and had a couple of mugs of Sea Slug's Surprise Pale Ale ready and waiting. This was going to be a "one-that-got-away" story to beat all. And so it was.

And now, children, it's time for you to snuggle down and go to sleep. Tomorrow you'll have to get up early, and I hope you have better luck than Thor did!

Chapter 10

THE COUNTERFEIT SUITOR

Hullo, children, I see that it's bedtime again! OK, snuggle down then, and I'll tell you a story about Frey. Yes, I know that I haven't said much about him, but your tender little ears might not be able to handle most of his stories. But there is one good story which I think I can get away with telling you.

Once upon a time, Frey was idly flipping through a pile of magazines which were on the counter at The Valhalla Sports Bar and Grill. These magazines were the type that come in plain brown wrappers, but even so, Odin had to have his subscription sent to The Valhalla rather than to his home. Frey was always on the lookout for someone "to audition", as he put it, and these magazines were his best sources of new talent. Yes, children, Frey was into plays and acting. He was awesome at foreplays, which made him *very* popular with the ladies. Which four plays? Heh, heh, heh, um, er . . . yes, there was the Scottish Ploy . . . er, *Play*, the Norman Play, the Russian Play, and the Varangian Play. He was *very* good at it, too, and usually got to perform every night. There were matinees, too . . . as I said, Frey was very, *very* popular!

Well, Odin wasn't around, so Frey hopped into Odin's favorite custom-built chair, the one with the little brass "Hlidskjalf Manufacturing Company" plaque on the back. That was the comfiest chair in the place, and ol' One-Eye didn't like it at all if other folks dared to sit in it. So that was why Frey had to keep glancing up to see if and when the boss-man was coming back.

On one of those glances, his eyes registered a remarkable sight. Frey didn't look back down at his magazine again, which was open to Miss July. Instead, he just stared at this vision which undulated gracefully along the sidewalk just outside the open front door of The Valhalla. Frey's eyes bugged out . . . this one beat Miss July all hollow! He *had* to get her name, her telephone number, her front door key . . . and just as he bailed out of Odin's chair, Odin himself came in the door with Frigg and the Norn sisters. Frey quickly tried to dodge around them to get to the door so's he could find that beautiful girl again, but he was too late. The only folks on the sidewalk were blind Hod who was hopefully holding a horn full of swizzle sticks for sale, three chickens, and a bug. No beautiful blondes. Frey just stood there, anxiously looking around, but no luck. His hope collapsed slowly; maybe he'd been daydreaming. If so, it was sure a vivid dream! She was so . . . so . . . sssso . . . .Frey lost his momentary composure and his hope once again began to rise.

Just then, Skirnir, Frey's publicist, came around the corner, holding a sheaf of paper. He looked at Frey, looked again, whistled, and smiled broadly. Skirnir was always *very* happy when Frey was in high spirits like that. The only catch was that Frey was usually chasing after some dumb blonde, rather than paying attention to Skirnir. Oh, well, you can't get lucky all the time! But this acting contract he was bringing to Frey was at least something better than appearing in a toothpaste commercial. Skirnir trotted up to Frey to hand him the contract for approval.

Frey just sort of looked vaguely at it, and then his eyes wandered back to where he'd last seen this beautiful maiden, this totally incredible female, this lusciously rounded and curvaceous beauty, this . . . this . . . . At this point, Skirnir realized that Frey was in lust . . . er, in love again, and that he'd better hold onto the contract until Frey came back down to earth.

"Did you *see* her?" Frey asked in a stunned voice.

"No", said Hod and Skirnir in chorus. Then Hod continued, "But she had these clicking type of shoes, sorta went tapitty tapitty on the sidewalk. Headed off toward Jotunheim, I think. I had a customer, so I can't be sure."

107

"Skirnir, I gotta find her! I *gotta*! You know all the Beautiful People, can you find out for me who she is?"

"Well, I don't usually go around chasing girls, but for you . . . for you, I would do simply *anything*!" Skirnir smoothed his exquisitely cut hair with one hand, while he stuffed the contract into the pocket of his gold velvet brocade lounging jacket with the other. A subtle waft of "My Sin" floated in the air as the publicist continued, "What do you want me to do when I find her?"

"First, get her telephone number, and then see if she'd be interested in going on a date with me," said our hero. "Maybe you could soften her up a little for me, too?"

"I'll try . . . I can't promise anything, but I'll do the best I can!"

Frey patted Skirnir on the shoulder and then dashed off to his country estate, where he started getting ready for the Big Date. Byggvir, the hired hand, would keep things under control while Frey was engaged in this latest pursuit. Byggvir was used to running the farm, and could be counted on to get top dollar for the stud fee for Frey's prizewinning boar, "Golden Bristles of Vanaheim". This made for a nice side-income, which helped pay for all those boxes of chocolates, bottles of champagne, perfume, those mink coats . . . . Frey happily rummaged through his guest closet, making sure that it would be ready for the next, hopefully long-term, guest. He was tired of one night stands; it was time for a serious relationship.

Meanwhile, Skirnir had to do a bit of sleuthing. Publicists get all the dirty work, as they will be glad to tell the world. A day passed, then two, then a week, then a month . . . and Frey got more and more antsy, wound-up, and anxious than anybody'd seen him in ages. By two months' time, he was downright moody and irritable. Nobody wanted him around; all he could talk about was this girl. Just to get some peace in Asgard, Odin sent the ravens and wolves out to look for her, but it was as if she never existed. Heimdall, too, came up dry, and he ran through the entire FBI database. Finally Njord got onto Skirnir's case, so the publicist himself had to actually go out looking for her. Njord had this sorta dockside aroma about him that Skirnir's My Sin couldn't even *begin* to cope with.

Skirnir had his own little spy network set up. He had to, in order to get the lowdown on the Beautiful People, to know where to drop his client's name, to grease the proper palms when Academy Award time came up . . . and before long a report came in from his friends the elves and fairies. It turned out that Frey's vision was the top supermodel in all Jotunheim. Gerd Gymirsdottir, her name was. She'd just returned home from a two-months-long shoot in Ulan Bator for a "Lingonberry Republic" catalogue . . . and the gnomes who knew her local house-elf had managed to get her unlisted phone number.

Skirnir gave this information to Frey, whose mood shifted in one nanosecond from grisly, grim, doom-and-despair to idiotically grinning bouncebouncebounce yaHOOO!!! He was all set to go running out the door to her place when Skirnir blocked the door.

"Whoa, not so fast, lover-boy! That really good acting contract I got for you, remember that one? You've gotta report to the lot today, or there'll be a multimillion dollar fine and I won't be able to get you anything better than dogfood ads in the future and I'll be ruined as a publicist and I'll never get a decent job again and . . . and . . . ." here, Skirnir broke down in uncontrollable sobbing.

"Oh, yeah. The contract." Frey thought hugely for a minute, and then his dazzlingly bright, slightly crooked boyish grin lit up the room. "Skirnir, why don't *you* go to her house and court her as my proxy? You're pretty good looking (here, Skirnir blushed and eyed Frey affectionately), I bet you could get her to come to Vanaheim for one of my famous candle-lit dinners for two . . . and then later maybe I could take her down to the north forty . . . that's pretty remote, and I can show her how the grain grows . . . ."

Skirnir rolled his eyes and grinned. "This time it's the grain? Last time it was the apple trees, before that, it was the alfalfa. I gotta remember some of these lines . . . . Oh, by the way, I'm gonna need to take some weaponry with me just in case; the house-elf says that her bodyguards mean business, and I'm not just going to saunter in there armed with only a nail file!"

Frey groaned with impatience and then offered Skirnir his competition Purdey's twelve gauge shotgun, the one with rose-wood grips and fancy silver inlay, the one which never seemed to miss the clay pigeon. Frey didn't have much in the way of weapons; he was a lover, not a fighter. Well, yes, children, he *did* do a few fight scenes in some of his movies, but that was mostly swash-buckling stuff, like Erroll Flynn. Skirnir also got the keys to Frey's Safari Land-Rover, as well as a generous expense account.

Well, children, you'd think that Skirnir had packed for a six-month expedition! Just the clothes alone took up two footlockers, four garment bags, and a large suitcase. But it didn't take him all that long to pack, and as the Rover's taillights faded into the distance, Frey was reporting to his new film director, a genial fellow named Geirr Lukas. This could be his big break, and he was itching for superstardom.

Skirnir got to the lady's well-guarded, reclusive palatial home at about suppertime. He was very good at planning his arrivals, and had timed this one beautifully. The only hitches he saw were the two slaveringly intent German shepherd guard dogs just behind the gate, and the bodyguard-*cum*-butler who looked as if he'd just been sprung from Joliet. There was also a shimmering force-field surrounding the grounds. But Skirnir had an "in" with the house-elf, who saw to a suitable diversion for the dogs and bodyguard, and who also showed Skirnir the secret tunnel which bypassed the force-field. Three minutes later, the publicist was knocking at the zebra-wood front door.

He knocked again, and the door swung open on well-oiled hinges. Standing there, clad in a white satin lounging gown with ostrich-feather trim and a plunging neckline which went all the way to . . . well, children, it was a *very* deep neckline, let's just leave it at that . . . was the beautiful Gerd. She looked Skirnir up and down, and then wrinkled her nose condescendingly at him. Skirnir explained his mission, with a lot of ums and ers along the way. He hadn't realized that a woman could be so entrancingly desirable, so spectacularly beautiful.

"Oh, *do* come on in, even though you are probably only a miserable paparazzi . . . or worse, a reporter for the tabloids! Just be sure that you spell my name right," the vision said, " . . . so you want me to travel all the way to Vanaheim to meet this stuck-up wanna-be actor of yours?"

"That's the general idea," the publicist mumbled, not taking his eyes off that neckline. He was beginning to regret that he wasn't her intended date. "Um..my friend says that he would *really* like to meet you in person . . . he said something about . . . ahem! . . . *auditioning* you for a really big role." His voice trailed off as he watched her every move as she welcomed him into her *sanctum sanctorum*. He didn't get around to mentioning the magic love-talisman that Frey had given him, the one that made any woman fall hopelessly in love with its bearer.

111

Gerd snorted indignantly. "Look, there are a lot of folks around here who'd love to have Frey's guts for garters. He's upstaged more good actors than I have hairs on my head!" (Here, Skirnir briefly looked at her coiffure before returning his attention to her neckline.) She continued, her voice softening into a coo, "I've *heard* about him . . . but tell me more about yourself, handsome!" The charm had begun its work, and Gerd was regarding Skirnir with growing approval. He wasn't bad looking, she thought, there are possibilities here that should be explored . . . . I think I'll give the servants the night off, and go slip into something a bit more comfy . . . .

She ushered him into the living room and gave him a horn of 20-year-old vintage mead that she'd been saving for an occasion like this. Ulan Bator had been profitable, but dull as mud, socially. As Skirnir sipped appreciatively, Gerd undulated into her bedroom and changed into her "comfy" outfit. What there was of it. When she made her grand entrance back into the living room, Skirnir had finished the horn and was pouring himself another. He nearly dropped the horn and the bottle when he saw her. He *did* drop his jaw . . . but not his eyes.

Children, here's where I have to skip a bit forward in time. Your Mom made me promise not to tell you some of the stuff that came next.

By the next morning, Skirnir was *really* regretting that he'd promised to turn Gerd over to Frey. He'd discovered a whole new world, a whole new dimension to the sweet mystery of life. But a promise is a promise, and Skirnir was a man of his word. Gerd suggested that Skirnir simply stay there at her house and take his own sweet time about returning to Vanaheim. But the publicist was adamant; he had to return. Gerd then promised to follow him to the ends of the earth, and ordered the servants to start packing for a long trip.

Skirnir got home somehow . . . he wasn't paying much attention to the road, but somehow didn't get too lost. Frey, fresh from the day's filming, anxiously asked him how it went. Skirnir hemmed and hawed and blushed and dug his toe in the dirt, and said that everything went fine, beyond his wildest dreams. This cheered up Frey so much that he went over to the phone to call off the next day's work. As he lifted the receiver, Skirnir said that Gerd would be along in a week or so; she had a *lot* to pack. Frey replaced the receiver and started pacing up and down, up and down, up and down.

"Look"' said Skirnir, "If you don't waste the director's time and keep your mind on what you're doing, you could be finished before she came, and you'd have a clear schedule! *Plus* a nice fat paycheck!"

This made excellent sense to Frey. He wasn't happy about the delay, but there was nothing he could do to hurry things along. He asked for his shotgun, Range Rover, and the amulet back, but Skirnir said that he'd earned them; that this had been a tough mission and that he'd barely escaped with his life and that as it was, he still could barely walk straight. After a bit of negotiating, Skirnir handed over the amulet, but got twenty-five percent of Frey's profit from this coming movie, plus the shotgun, plus the Rover. Frey was too edgy to argue well, so Skirnir made out very well on the deal.

The days passed on leaden feet. Frey finished his filming a day early, and spent the extra time shopping for a floor-length white mink coat and some other baubles. Skirnir was sent off on a month-long publicity tour . . . Frey had seen that hungry-puppy look in his eyes when he'd gotten back from his mission . . . and when Gerd finally arrived in her cream-colored stretch limo, Frey was ready. Oh, my, was he ready! And just in case, he had that amulet on a chain around his neck.

When Gerd saw Frey standing at his door, her heart gave a lurch, and she breathlessly ran toward him, all thoughts of Skirnir vanished in her desire to get to really know this incredibly handsome hunk of a man. That was *some* amulet, yah shure! Add to that Frey's natural talents, and, well, this story had a really happy ending. They announced their engagement the next morning, and the wedding was the day after.

I guess Skirnir had a lot of time to think about things, but when he got back, he was his old self again. The Riviera had agreed with him, and he'd made a lot of new friends there. Frey and Gerd were deliriously happy, especially since she was *very* fond of watching the grain grow down in the north forty.

Well, children, that's all for tonight. I think that I'm going to go take a nice cold shower and then toddle off to bed. Sweet dreams!

Chapter 11

SHOWDOWN AT THE
JOTUNHEIM CORRAL

L et's see what story I should tell you tonight . . . oh, you want something with some fighting in it? I think I could rustle up something in that department, children. There's a real rouser with Odin starting things off but Thor winds up having to come in and mop up afterwards. Sound good? OK, here goes.

It was a hot Monday afternoon in Asgard, and nothing was going on. Thor was off on an adventure someplace or other, Frigg and the girls were out "antique-ing", as they put it, and the Einherjar were watching the same reruns, playing the same old card games, and having the same old conversations. Odin sat glumly at the bar, sipping at a Bellywash Bitter Ale while flipping though an old dog-eared Louis Lamour western thriller which he'd already read at least fourteen times. There were no impending disasters, no tourists come to see the Sleipnir, The Amazing 8-Legged Horse, no nothing. The library was closed that day, the opera was in rehearsal, and Hod had left his usual post outside The Valhalla to take an afternoon siesta. Even the flies looked bored.

Odin decided to try an experiment. Those westerns always had cowboys riding on horses and having grand adventures. Why not lead Sleipnir out and try to break him to saddle? Sleipnir had grown from a gangly clumsy leggity grey colt to a handsome not-quite-so-clumsy leggity grey stallion. He had managed to learn how to walk after a fashion without getting tangled up and falling on his nose. Horse noses are very tender, so Sleipnir figured things out rather quickly. Remember, he was Loki's son. And Loki was one heckuva clever fella, yah, shure!

Already things were looking up. Odin got out his rattiest blue cloak and a ten-gallon cowboy hat which had been part of The Valhalla's "saloon-look" decor. He went out to the barn for a saddle and bridle, and then headed out back to the pasture where Sleipnir was busy sleeping under a tree. By the time the horse woke up, Odin had gotten him bridled and saddled. Odin could work very, very quickly when he wanted to, and casting that sleep spell on the horse didn't hurt, either. Sleipnir was used to Odin by now, but not to this funny thing strapped to his back. He hopped around, bucked, got tangled up, fell on his nose, got to his feet, and gave Odin a dirty look. Sleipnir was a very, *very* smart horse, and he could feel the magic in the saddle. Better to go along with things for now, and deal with Odin at a later time.

Sleipnir was in for a few more surprises. First, Odin swung onto his back, just like in the old Hopalong Cassidy oaters. And as the god settled into the saddle, Sleipnir felt the magic tingle and whirl about him, and suddenly the horse felt as light as a feather. He took one step and then another . . . and his legs weren't threatening to get tangled up. He moved into a trot . . . and it was like magic how nimble he had suddenly become. Of course, it *was* magic; Odin had no intentions of falling off and getting kicked by four hind feet. Sleipnir was thrilled. He could run, *really* run, run so fast that he flew. Literally. No wings, even. The stallion had never known such freedom, such exhilaration, such joy in running. Odin, meanwhile, whirled his cowboy hat around his head and screamed "Hi-Yo, Sllleipniiiiirrrrrr!" as the two of them careered around in the sky, diving through clouds and startling the vultures down at the Asgard Dump.

Odin was really happy about how things were working out, too. He now had a flight-capable means of transportation which was even faster than Thor's Harley. Sleipnir had to be the fastest horse in all of the Nine Worlds! Odin smiled as he got a sudden thought. He didn't dare open his mouth to laugh while facing forward, since the speed of Sleipnir's flight meant that a 150 mph. wind was hitting the god's face. It would have blown his mouth open, inflated his cheeks like balloons, and dried his tongue out before he could get it closed again. But he could smile OK, which is just what he did. Why not challenge the meanest, biggest, hairiest giant in Jotunheim to a horse race? That would be a junk dealer named Hrungnir, he had a horse that he was pretty proud of. And with a really interesting bet on things, Odin anticipated making a sizeable bank deposit the next morning plus get another horse. Money always got Odin excited, especially if it was coming to him. So far, only Odin knew about Sleipnir's newfound dexterity and speed. Ol' "One-Eye" didn't like to bet on dice that weren't loaded in his favor, and in this case he felt he had a sure thing.

So Odin had Sleipnir fly a circuitous route to Hrungnir's Junkyard. He didn't want the Jotun to see his horse in action until it was too late. He managed to land Sleipnir before the dogs started barking . . . every good junkyard has dogs, and Hrungnir had a pack of the ugliest, meanest curs you could imagine. Big yellow and grey ones with mad yellow eyes and impressive yellow teeth. They piled up on the chain-link fence on the inside, howling maniacally and gnawing ferociously at the metal and trying their utmost best to scrabble their way through so they could savage this trespasser and the horse he rode in on. Odin dismounted as Hrungnir emerged from the back of the lot where he'd been sorting recyclable plastics. The Jotun was in a foul mood because he'd just sorted a gallon jug which had had honey in it, hadn't been washed, and which as a result had been loaded with yellowjackets.

119

"(A long string of unprintable words!!!)" screamed the Jotun as he picked the last of the insects off his face, "You (bleeepity-bleeping bleep-bleep) dogs, SHADDAP!!!" A chorus of yelps and screams answered him as the rest of the yellowjackets who'd missed their turn at the giant decided to mix it up with the dogs. Odin hastily erected a magical "repel stinging insects" shield around himself and Sleipnir. Neither horse nor god really wanted to get closer to the fence because the dogs were twice as angry now. Hrungnir very quickly climbed over the chain-link fence and dashed over to where Odin and Sleipnir were standing in order to get away from the dog-wasp mixture.

"Howdy, stranger!" growled the giant, "Yew come fer yer funeral? Ah'm feelin' kinda mean rat now, so Ah kin oblige yuh rat heer on thuh spot!"

Odin, who'd pulled his white Stetson down low over his face, merely smiled and looked dangerous. Actually, the Stetson was more sort of a greyish yellow thanks to all the cigar smoke in The Valhalla, but once upon a time it had been pure white. Sleipnir stumbled up to his side, also looking dangerous. Or as dangerous as he could while trying to save himself from falling on his nose. Turned out, the horse realized, that he could only run or fly if Odin and his magic were actually on his back.

The giant looked at Odin wrapped in his moth-eaten faded blue cloak which had a big rip in the hem, looked at this freak of a horse, and started laughing in spite of himself. Here was somebody who was even more miserable and silly-looking than he was!

"That's some cayuse yuh got there, podnuh!" he chortled, "Betcha couldn't beat mah hoss Goldilocks! Har, har, har!"

"Wanna bet?" asked Odin quietly, and the bet was on. The

Jotun knew darn well that his championship Palomino could easily beat this misbegotten bangtail without breaking a sweat. He also anticipated a tidy deposit to his bank account in the morning, as well as a "dogfood horse". Those hounds ate a ton of meat a day, but all those leg bones should keep them busy for quite a while.

Well, children, they mounted up, Odin said "Get ready, get set, GO!", and off they went. Turned out that Goldilocks also had a magic spell on him, and he raised dirt rooster-tails as he sped up to 100 miles an hour. Sleipnir, with Odin and his magic aboard, took to the sky and raised the ante to 110 mph., which Goldilocks matched and surpassed. On they went, breaking Mach One just as they got to the walls of Asgard. Heimdall barely had time to blink as the sonic boom rattled his toll booth and set off all the alarms, whistles, sirens, and klaxons mounted in and on the booth. The spells on the horses let them stop on a dime without their riders shooting off their backs and landing splat! on the Asgard Wall. And children, it turned out that Sleipnir had just beaten Goldilocks to the wire by one swollen nose.

"Dang it, that's *some* hoss yuh got there . . . hey, you (highly colorful descriptive phrase) *cheated*! Yuh used *magic* on thet thar hoss! Ah'm gonna beat yuh up an' rip yer guts out and feed 'em to muh *dawgs!!!*"

"Hold on, there, pardner, come on in and have a drink on the house . . . the livery stable will take care of your horse. Free drinks! All you want!"

Odin had the Jotun there. Hrungnir was parched. Even if it meant going into Asgard, into The Valhalla . . . the lure of free drinks, all he could hold . . . and so the Jotun handed over the reins to the kid at the livery stable and followed Odin into the bar. The Einherjar, who had been almost as bored as Odin, grabbed

121

whatever weapons came to hand in the happy anticipation of a knock-down drag-out saloon brawl. Odin whipped off his hat so that the boys could see who he was, and shouted "STOP!!!" It was almost comical to see the boys freeze in place, some holding bar stools over their heads by two legs, others with hastily-broken bottles, and a few with the usual spears, daggers, axes, and bludgeons. Only a slow drip-drip-drip sound could be heard from the broken bottles. Even the flies stopped in mid-air. When the Boss spoke like that, it was time to *freeze*.

Odin grabbed a bottle of "Old Rattail File" and a glass from the counter and poured Hrungnir a Herculean jolt. He handed the glass to the giant, who knocked it back, grimaced, coughed, and held the glass out for a refill. The piano player in the corner immediately started playing again, and the flies "unfroze" and continued on their way. The Einherjar sheepishly put down their armaments . . . after all, the Boss was treating this dude to a snort . . . so it must be OK.

Some of the Valkyries came in to get ready for the night's concert. The Valhalla had a small stage on one side of the large bar-room, which was already set up with 14-foot high stacks of high-performance speakers, the sort you find at football stadiums. Stadia. Whatever. Each night, the Valkyries performed for the boys, usually heavy metal, punk rock, and R&B. The Valkyries, an all-girl band, were quite versatile, especially if there was a lot of screaming in the music. When they weren't performing, they waited on tables and stopped fights. Nobody wanted to get tossed out by a female bouncer, so the Einherjar were usually pretty well-behaved.

Well, one drink led to another, and before long, Hrungnir was going through the stuff by the case. He also couldn't seem to stop bragging about how he was going to pound Odin into a flat red pancake and blow up Asgard with some nitroglycerine he had handy which was well past its expiration date, and Asgard would be a nice place to toss it, he opined. Pretty soon the Valkyries started shuttling booze to him, hoping that he'd get so drunk that he'd pass out and they could get on with their concert. When they had to go change into costume, Freyja continued pouring, trying to avoid the giant's clumsy efforts to pinch her fanny. The boys couldn't give him the bum's rush since he was officially Odin's guest, and back then folks took hospitality very seriously.

It was not a pleasant evening. The Valkyries did their best, but even with the speakers cranked up to the max, they had a hard time drowning out Hrungnir's loud drunken bragging and threats aimed at Asgard and all who lived in it. He was out his best horse, his profits from the junkyard for a month, and his pride. But as long as he was Odin's guest, he was perfectly safe from folks ganging up on him and kicking him out of The Valhalla.

At about one in the morning, Thor came in, swinging his hammer, complaining that folks wanted to sleep, and that if Odin didn't turn down the speakers he'd turn them off for good. He then noticed Hrungnir slumped at the bar, screaming epithets at the top of his foghorn voice. A Jotun in The Valhalla???? Thor stamped over and grabbed the giant by his big red nose and said, "Who the heck are you?" (or words to that effect) and the giant said "Hrungnir, and whasss (hic!) it to yuh? Hic?" (or words to that effect) and Thor said "I don't like your face; why don't you take it home!" (or words to that effect) and the giant said "I'm going to beat your stupid brains in!" (or words to that effect) and then Odin suggested that they take this discussion outside (or words to that effect).

The upshot was that Thor and Hrungnir would meet out at the corral behind Hrungnir's place at high noon the next day and settle things for good. Hela had time to get a concession stand set up at a safe distance, with caramel corn, devil dogs, coffin-shaped black

Mylar balloons, and soft drinks for the kiddies. Hod was perfectly happy to run it, since everybody would be there which meant that there would be no business in front of The Valhalla. Hela, meanwhile, got ready for the inevitable funeral, and even had a coffin discreetly on site, disguised as a cooler full of beer.

As the clock's hands approached noon (yes, Hela had also brought that big black grandfather clock from the Hell-Hole Funeral Home, the one which ticked away the last minutes like a slow, inevitable, heavy heartbeat) (that clock could only measure last minutes, not middle ones or beginning ones), everybody started looking for hiding places. Frey and Gerd found a wrecked van, shooed out the rats, and claimed it for their own. Yes, children, the springs still worked just fine. And Frigg got all the womenfolk she could find to boil water, rip up sheets, and clean up a back shed as a makeshift field hospital. Odin, who'd started all this, was nowhere to be seen. Loki worked the crowd taking bets until Hoenir and Tyr grabbed him and hogtied him to Hrungnir's trash compacter. Sif laughed to see Loki with the other rats and maggots, and then went to help Frigg. The Einherjar salted themselves around the site in strategic locations just in case Hrungnir started getting the better of the thunder god.

The deck was stacked, the players were set, and Hela's clock mournfully bonged out twelve lugubrious doom-laden notes. What's that, children? Oh, you'll have to look that up tomorrow in the dictionary. Long words are good for you! Let's see, where were we? Oh, yes, as the last note died out, the air seemed as heavy as lead. Not a soul was stirring except for Loki, who was desperately trying to chew through his gag, which tasted like fuel oil. No breeze, no crickets, no birdsong. Just the slow, heavy tread of Hrungnir's boots crunching on the gravel.

The giant was clad entirely in black. He had an Uzi disguised as a whetstone in his holster, and his mean yellowish bloodshot eyes swept back and forth, looking for his enemy. Hung over, Hrungnir looked even grimmer than usual, which was pretty grim to start with. His left hand twitched over the holster, ready to draw and fire if so much as a mouse twitched its nose.

No, children, I don't know why they kept disguising machine guns as whetstones. Yes, a banana would work just as well, but it seemed that if it looked like a whetstone, it couldn't *possibly* be anything else. Anyhow, Hrungnir was ready and waiting for action. He also had a sidekick, some fella called "Foggy", who'd been foisted off on him by the other Jotuns. Sort of a Gabby Hayes type, but nowhere near as brave. Heck, "Foggy" had feet of clay, and as soon as Hrungnir had adopted The Stance, he'd fainted dead away. The Jotun was all alone there, waiting for Thor to show up.

Suddenly the ear-shattering sound of twin tuned mufflers roared and echoed in the junkyard. Then there was a screeching sound as of a Harley coming to a halt on the far side of one of the bigger piles of junk. Hrungnir whirled and faced that direction, hand at the ready. Then Thjalfi, Thor's favorite mechanic, poked his head around another pile of junk and shouted out, "Hey, Hrungnir! Thor's gonna cheat and come at you from underneath! He'll nail you before your weapon clears leather!"

Hrungnir, convinced that of *course* Thor would cheat . . . he *was* one of those rascally Æsir, after all . . . grabbed a biggish piece of plate steel, the type they make battleship hulls out of, from the nearest scrap metal pile. He threw it flat on the earth, jumped on top of it and sneered at the mechanic and the invisible crowd.

"All right, yuh mizzerble chunk of buzzard-bait! C'mon and face me, or are yuh *yellow*? Ah'm *waiiii—tinggg!*"

Suddenly Thor stepped out from behind a third pile of junk, screamed "*INCOMMINNGGG*!!!", and threw his hammer at the Jotun. At the same time, Hrungnir grabbed his "whetstone" and got off a burst just before his head was smashed like a jar of strawberry jam. See, children, I worked that jar you dropped this morning into the story! Took your Mom almost half an hour to clean it up, too! Well, it took Hela about the same time to clean up Hrungnir.

Anyway, some of the bullets had struck the incoming hammer and ricocheted all over the place. One clipped the rope binding Loki so that he was able to wiggle free and Get Out Of Dodge as fast as he could scamper. Other slugs whined off all over the Nine Worlds, but one kept coming straight at Thor's forehead. Now, the gods had thick skulls, and Thor had a thicker skull than most, but even he could get hurt by a machine-gun bullet fired at him at point-blank range.

It looked at first like a double kill. The giant fell forward on top of Thor, and there was blood all *over* the place. The women rushed out to the battlefield with the hot water and torn sheets, ready to do a Florence Nightingale number on the wounded. Hela also came forward, to deal with the dead.

At first, it looked as if Hela would have all the business to herself. Then Thor groaned in pain and the women all tried to pull the body of the giant off him. Most of the menfolk had hot-footed it back to Asgard in case the giants attacked it. The only one who'd stayed in Asgard was Heimdall, and he could only guard one point of access at a time. Nobody really wanted to disturb Frey at that particular moment, and Hod was busy running Hela's concession stand.

Suddenly, Sif looked up and noticed a little boy who was pointing his finger and going "Bang! Bang!" at the giant. The kid looked an awful lot like Thor, too. No beard, of course, but the same red hair, the same crazy hairstyle, the same overmuscled build. Aha, she thought, must be one of the twins! Before he'd met Sif, Thor had had a brief fling with a Jotun gal who made iron knives and axes for a living . . . she had her own forge . . . but that ended when he and Sif became an item. Thor paid child support and visited the twins when he could, and their mother wasn't too angry at the thunder god for moving on. Anyway, Sif called out to Magni (she could tell him from Modi by now) to help them move the carcass off Thor and onto Hela's "meat wagon". Magni had inherited his father's strength, which had made him the terror of his schoolyard. He pushed the giant off his father with no trouble, and then the women were all over the thunder god with clean pieces of sheet dipped in boiling water. Sif shouted to Magni to go get a doctor, fast! and Magni scooted off on Thor's bike, Thjalfi in hot pursuit.

Magni was back less than ten minutes later with Dr. Groa Rasmussen hanging onto him in sheer terror. Magni managed to detach her and get her to Thor, who was trying to get to his feet. Dr. Rasmussen got some injectable morphine into the thunder god, and then told everyone that she'd have to operate there on the spot, that it was too dangerous to move him. The ladies wound up trying to build an impromptu operating room around doctor and patient out of sheets that hadn't been torn up yet and some broken curtain rods. Dr. Rasmussen had been a field medic in the Marines, and battlefield "meatball" surgery was one of her specialties. She poured a bottle of alcohol over Thor's head (Thor sucked down what he could reach with his tongue), apologized for not having much in the way of anaesthesia, and gave Thor another bottle of alcohol to keep him busy while she worked.

Children, I'm not going to go into the medical procedure that took place, since I'm not a brain surgeon. But Dr. Rasmussen managed to get the bullet almost out of Thor's skull by the time the thunder god finished the bottle. He started thanking her and saying that he'd just met her husband. This surprised the doctor, who'd been told that he was missing in action ten years before, and was presumed dead. He'd even been awarded a posthumous Congressional Medal of Honor. Thor looked surprised by this statement . . . it could be that the sensation of the doctor messing about with his frontal lobes had something to do with this expression . . . and then mentioned that he'd seen Colonel Auvandil Rasmussen just the other night. He'd apparently been assigned to a top secret mission in Thule, Greenland, and then his records had somehow gotten mislaid. Outside of losing one toe to frostbite, he was fine, and should be showing up at the Rasmussen home that very evening. Dr. Groa Rasmussen was so excited about this that she stopped what she was doing and started crying with relief and joy.

"Hey!" croaked Thor, "What about the bullet? Couldja please

finish getting it out of my head so that you can sew me up before the alcohol wears off?"

But Groa was shaking so badly that she couldn't hold a coffee cup, much less a scalpel aimed at Thor's grey matter. She simply couldn't steady herself enough to finish the extraction, but at least the bullet was out of the brain proper and was merely rattling around in the space between the brain and the skull. She did manage to get the thunder god bandaged up with the help of Sif and Frigg, gave him a bottle of Excedrin, and told him that he'd have to deal with the occasional headache. Then she collared Modi who took her back home for the reunion with her long-lost and dearly beloved husband.

Thjalfi, meanwhile, had gotten Frey and Gerd's van running, and they loaded Thor in it, as well as Sif and Frigg as nurses. Frey and Gerd were too tired at that point to walk all the way back to Asgard, so they went along for the ride, too. Everyone got back to Asgard OK, and the giants didn't attack. Since Hrungnir had died with no will, Hela acquired ownership of his junkyard, dogs and all, in lieu of payment for her services. She was then able to turn around and sell it within the week to the Muspellheim Crematorium and Brickworks, Inc. for a tidy profit. Odin brought Goldilocks back to Asgard, where he had him trained for the racetrack. If you children look hard enough, you might even find him listed in the racing pages.

Nobody ever bet against Odin on horses after that. And Loki, who would normally bet on anything, refused to bet against his own flesh and blood, especially since Sleipnir had proved he could run so fast. It was generally agreed that Sleipnir was the best of all horses, and that tourists would come from far and wide now to see him and to buy a few drinks at The Valhalla. The Einherjar drank to that, drank to Thor's health, and then raised a horn to Odin, for enlivening an otherwise dull day in Asgard.

And so, children, that's how come Thor sometimes gets a splitting headache and has to go knocking down trees and sizzling golfers who insist on playing through during thunderstorms. Now go to sleep, and tomorrow morning, please try not to break anything else as you're running out to catch the school bus!

Chapter 12

THOR AND THE MASKED MADWOMEN

Hello, there, children! Hey! Put down that pillow! It's not *nice* to try to hit your Uncle Einar like that . . . your Uncle Einar knows a few tricks he learned a looonnnnggg time ago which you might not want to see him try on you! You *do* want a story, tonight, don't you? OK, that's better, snuggle down there, and we'll pick up all those feathers tomorrow.

It wasn't long after Thor got hurt out at Hrungnir's Junkyard that he got this "get well" card from an "anonymous friend," which had a ticket in it for a JJWF Wrestling Championship . . . oh, that's "Jotunheim Jiant Wressling Federation" . . . you know that most of the Jotuns can't spell their own names, much less simple words like "cat" and "dog". So it's "Jiant" and "Wressling". I'm really surprised that they got "Federation" right! Well, anyway, this ticket fell out of the envelope into Thor's lap. Thor was at home . . . the Thrudheim Athletic Club *was* his home, gym, training center, place to store stuff, and locker room. He was in kind of a nasty mood, as he had one of these headaches . . . ever since that slug had hit him, he got these migraines which felt as if someone was twisting a rat-tail file right through his head, front to back, about two inches above his eyebrows. He was also in a nasty mood because he was supposed to take it easy following the brain surgery to try to get the slug out. Thor *hated* having to take it easy. Only the threat of Frigg and Sif and "the girls" coming over to nurse and coo over him if he didn't take it easy kept the thunder god from stomping out to look for something to fry, smash, demolish, crush, obliterate, or trash.

The JJWF ticket looked like just the ticket outta there. It was for a ringside seat, with complementary beverages and snacks. Plus autographs of all contestants. Thor studied the handwriting on the card and envelope to see if he could figure out who'd sent him the card. He was able to rule out Sif or Frigg or any other member of the Asgard Volunteer Medical Association. Frey and Gerd were out of the country on their weekly honeymoon. Njord was out at sea; the cod were running. Odin? Naah, he wasn't the card-sending type. Well, whatever . . . the headache was threatening to blow Thor's head off, so the thunder god swallowed half a bottle of Excedrin and went outside for a short stroll in the sunshine. The match was for the next night, at someplace called "Geirrod's Backdoor Arena" in Jotunheim. Time enough to saunter over there on foot. Riding the Harley would be noisy and bumpy, which wouldn't be at all good, headache-wise.

Thor'd gotten across Bifrost and was picking his way across a rocky field when Loki suddenly showed up. Thor looked at Loki sourly until he saw that he was holding a bright red ticket to the wrestling match. Loki was also wearing one of the loudest sport jackets Thor had ever had the misfortune of seeing . . . it was so loud that Thor had to turn his eyes away from Loki lest his headache get even worse. And that's how come Thor missed the gloating sneer on Loki's face.

"Where'd *you* get that ticket from?" asked the thunder god incuriously.

"Won it in a crap game," Loki lied, "I hear it's the Masked Madwomen tonight, teaming up against the Mystery Marauder".

Now actually, children, it had been Loki who'd sent that "get well" card and the ticket to Thor. Loki had gotten into one of his scrapes not long before . . . he'd disguised himself as a little birdie to spy on The Masked Madwomen . . . they were actually Geirrod's daughters . . . as they were training. Anything to get an edge, gambling-wise. Geirrod's silent intruder alarm had gone off, which meant that the Jotun was able to saunter out of the training hall, cut around back, and put the arm on Loki. Loki, still disguised as a little birdie, had been tossed into an empty (but recently used) garbage can, and the lid tamped down hard. It was a magic garbage can, too; Loki couldn't change back into his real form, force the lid off, and get away.

Geirrod was not a nice Jotun. He'd left Loki in there to stew in that trash can in the August sun for what seemed to be a month or three, with no food or water. Yah, Loki could try to pick at some of the things remaining in the garbage can, but he didn't really want to. The can had been sitting outside in the hot sun for a rather longish time before Loki'd been tossed into it. Just standing on/in the stuff in the bottom of the can was bad enough.

After too long, Geirrod had opened the can and grabbed Loki, still disguised as a little birdie, around the neck. He raised the birdie up to his eyes, squeezing more and more tightly. Loki managed to squeak out "I'm Loki!" before passing out. The giant slackened his grip just enough to let Loki get some air, and then started grinning evilly. His piggish eyes turned up at the corners as he began to laugh.

"Haaaw haaaaawwwww*snurk*hawwwwww! Loki, eh? Snurf, snurf, *snurk* haawwwww!" Geirrod, contrary to most folks' opinions of him, actually had an I.Q. over 70. Not *much*

135

higher, true. But he had enough smarts to get an Idea. Here he had Loki in his total power. Loki could be convinced with little effort to do *exactly* what the Jotun wanted. And Geirrod, who was Hrungnir's brother, and who'd been cut out of Hrungnir's inheritance by Hela, wanted to get back at Thor for his part in Hrungnir's death. Opportunity had Knocked. Geirrod grinned wickedly as he brought Loki's beady little birdie eyes close to his own beady big eyes.

"Loki, you're gonna do me a little favor if I let you go!" Geirrod chuckled deep in his hairy chest as he tickled Loki's feathers with the point of a razor-sharp hunting knife. "You're gonna get Thor to come to me here in Jotunheim, tomorrow night, without fail, and you're gonna make *sure* that Thor comes here without his hammer, and without that championship "muscle" belt he likes to wear. Got it?" The giant raised the tip of the knife to hover over Loki's left eye, at about a half millimeter from the cornea. What's that, children? Oh, a millimeter is about the thickness of a really *thin* piece of Swiss cheese. Which means that the knife tip was almost touching Loki's eye.

Loki gulped hard. Separating Thor from either his belt or his hammer was going to be tricky, if not impossible. But not as impossible as keeping alive if Geirrod felt like skewering him with that knife or squeezing him into paste. Geirrod's grip was tightening; Loki had a half-second left before Lights Out. "I agree!!!" he gasped with what he hoped wouldn't be his last breath. The giant's grip eased, and the knife went away. Geirrod grinned evilly at the little birdie as he laid a first-class geas on it. What's that? Children, a geas is a magic spell that makes whomever it's cast on *have* to do some task. Geirrod was used to getting his own way, thanks to that spell. And it looked as if he was going to get his way again with Loki. Revenge was gonna be sweet.

So he let Loki go, gave Loki the two tickets for the wrestling match, and told Loki that Thor had better be there Or Else. Which meant that Loki had to catch Thor unawares. Which meant waiting for a headache. But if Loki just happened to have a finely-tuned ultrasonic transmitter aimed at Thor's head, maybe he could induce a whopper of a migraine, which meant that Thor wouldn't be thinking straight, which meant that Loki might be able to pull this off.

And this is how come Loki and Thor were headed toward Geirrod's Backdoor Arena, holding tickets to the JJWF match. And also how come Thor didn't have his hammer or his belt with him. All the thunder god was wearing was a pair of sweat pants, a sweatshirt advertising the "Battlefield Kill Café", and a pair of flip-flop sandals. Plus, of course, his shades and his Asgard Express Card. And as the two of them walked in the fresh air, Thor's headache slowly started going away.

The two travelers got as far as Grid's Motel and Cat House when the sun began setting. Grid was a buxom, cheerful Jotun who welcomed them both inside. She was able to provide a lovely candle-lit meal of oysters accompanied by chilled champagne, and showed them photos of some of her "daughters" and "sisters", who also happened to be staying there at the motel. Thor was thirsty after his headache, and did justice to the champagne. Grid had made sure to get her paws on his Asgard Express Card right off the bat, so she didn't mind bringing in case after case of the really expensive stuff. Loki managed to get through the better part of one bottle before he toppled off his chair backwards, plowed to the gills.

The oysters worked just fine, and before long, Thor and Grid were sharing a big, long cigar. No, children, Thor didn't usually smoke, but this was an unusual circumstance, and he didn't inhale.

137

Actually, Grid smoked most of the cigar, OK? And for a Jotun, she was really nice and friendly. She'd known many of the Æsir and Vanir, especially the menfolk, for a number of years, and she held no grudges against Thor. In fact, she told Thor that she'd heard that this wrestling match had been set up with the express purpose of getting rid of him. Grid heard everything; her sisters and daughters told her lots of things that they'd heard from their boyfriends and other acquaintances. This also helped Grid maintain her cover as a motel-keeper. Heimdall came by every so often to debrief her and to give her new instructions. But she didn't tell Thor that she was an FBI agent.

What she did tell Thor was what little she'd heard. She also loaned him a Kevlar bullet-proof vest, a pair of titanium-steel gauntlets, a fully-charged power-pack mounted on a belt, and a laser gun which could punch a hole through three feet of case-hardened steel. The vest wouldn't show under Thor's sweatshirt; the gauntlets were disguised to look like biker's gloves, and the belt (with holster and laser gun) looked like a sport fanny pack with a water bottle and other hiker's accessories. Thor thanked her again and again, which pleased Grid so much that she decided not to charge Thor for the evening's food and entertainment.

The next morning, Thor and Loki were ready to head on out to the arena. Loki wondered why Grid seemed to be so friendly towards Thor . . . she hugged him and kissed him and made him promise to stop by any time he was in the neighborhood. Or even remotely *near* the neighborhood. They had some problems crossing a river along the way, thanks to one of Geirrod's daughters who had been lying in wait to ambush them, but Thor let her have one burst of high-intensity coherent light, and suddenly there were no problems crossing the river. Loki was startled to see this, as he'd promised Geirrod that Thor would come to the arena unarmed and unsuspicious. He didn't dare question Thor, because that would give the game away. No, Loki couldn't breathe a whisper about having met Geirrod before . . . and so he had to frantically begin to concoct some kind of plausible story in his mind to tell Geirrod, explaining Thor's new armament. Thor hauled himself out of the river with the help of a low branch of a rowan tree growing on the bank. He shook himself like a dog and continued on his way, leaving Loki to climb up the steep river-bank by himself.

Thor wasn't all that unsuspicious, especially after the chat with Grid. Loki *had* to be involved in this somehow. He watched Loki carefully and discreetly out of the corner of his eyes as they walked along. They finally got to Geirrod's Backdoor Arena shortly before the wrestling match was going to take place. Thor, as usual, had gotten lost and had refused to ask directions. Loki, of course, couldn't tell Thor the correct directions, because then Thor would ask Loki how he knew how to get to the arena, and then Loki would be in serious trouble with Thor. It was obvious that Thor was on guard, and so Loki had to do best to pretend to be absolutely innocent.

Geirrod's Backdoor Arena was a dump of a place. It's the type of place that any self-respecting thug or gambler would want to stay away from. Rats scampered among rotting piles of garbage outside the windows, and the place smelled like a goat pen. Thor pushed open the doors and went inside. Loki suddenly said that he had to go wash his hands, and left at a dead run headed away from the Arena.

The place was dim inside, but a gnarly, ancient usher showed Thor to his seat. The ring was suddenly lit up by torches, and Thor settled back, one hand on the handle of the laser gun just in case. Suddenly, a loudspeaker blared "BE AFRAID . . . BE *VERRRRY* AFRAID! THE MASKED MADWOMENNNN, CHAMPEEENS OF THE RINNNG, ARE HERE TO TAKE ON ANNNNY COMERS! THE MMMASKED MADWOMENNN HAVE *NEVERRRR* BEEN DEFEATEDDD! THEIR POWWER COMES FROM THE MYSTIC ORRB OF THE GIANTS, WHICH CHOSE THEMMM ALONNNE TO INHERIT THE STRENNGTH OF THE GODDS!" Then, two tall figures, masked and cloaked in black, swirled into the ring. They shed their cloaks, revealing two of the most muscular female bodies Thor had ever seen. Like, each one looked like Mr. Olympus! Their biceps were huge, their triceps and quadriceps even larger. They wore skimpy little black leather and chain outfits and hobnailed jackboots. Their oiled bodies shone in the lights as they posed and snarled at the audience.

Suddenly, the chair Thor was sitting in was propelled into the ring by a big spring which had been under it, and which had been released by one of Geirrod's crew. This meant that Thor suddenly found himself falling into the ring toward the two ladies . . . and as he flipped himself around to land on his feet, he noticed that they had filed their teeth to points.

Children, this was one of the most exciting wrestling matches I've ever seen! Thor learned all about various maneuvers with the colorful names "Samoan Surfboard", "Body Slam", "Airplane Spin", and "Cross-Face Chicken Wing". As the audience roared its approval of the level of violence, Thor taught one Masked Madwoman a cute little sequence called "Backbreaker" followed immediately by "Body Slam", after which he jumped up and down on her a few times. As for the other Madwoman, Thor first broke his chair over her head, then showed her that he'd learned how to do the Flying Surfboard, and finally he piledrove her through the ring floor.

As the first Madwoman tried to claw her way to her feet, Thor met her chin with his knee, propelling her up and out of the ring. She landed about six rows back in the audience. Thor whirled around, grabbed the second Madwoman, showed her a new variation of the Airplane Spin . . . he grabbed her by her waist, raised her over his head, and spun her around as fast as he could. When the Madwoman reached about 300 rpm, Thor tried for a distance launch. If it hadn't been for the wall she punched through, she might have gone over a hundred feet. As it was, she landed amidst a pile of splinters about fifteen feet away from the Arena. Thor clasped both hands together and raised them over his head, screaming in victory.

"HOLLLD IT, BIG BOY! IT IS NOW TIME FORRR YOUU TO MEET YOURRRRR DOOOOOMMMMM . . . THE UNNNNNDERTAKER IS WAITINGGGG FOR YOUUUU! ANNND HEEERREEEE HEEE COMMMMES! GEIRRROD THE GRISLYYYY COMMMES FORRR YOURRR HEARRRT!" Thor whirled around, hunkering down and looking for his next opponent. His laser gun was in his hand, the power pack had been switched on, and its eerie whine had ascended into the "ready to discharge" range. Thor was as ready as he could be, which was a good thing for him. Geirrod was inside a tank, and had a HEAT round loaded and aimed at the thunder god.

The turret cannon fired at Thor, who was literally at point-blank range. But the thunder god, who had one hand free, was able to catch the incoming round just before it hit his chest. It was handy being a god sometimes. Gods could do things like that. Thor then fired the laser at the tank's turret, followed by throwing the HEAT round right through the hole that the laser had burned. The tank then demonstrated a maneuver called "catastrophic kill", in which the turret goes straight up on a column of flame as the

ammo inside the tank cooks off. That took care of a good portion of the arena's roof. The rest of the arena was demolished as the audience all tried to run away from Thor as fast as they could and as quickly as possible. Thor, meanwhile, cheerfully added to the destruction until his power pack went dead.

Thor was happy. His headache was gone, and he'd just had a pleasant afternoon packed with action. He'd worked off all the depression he'd been under since that episode at Hrungnir's Junkyard, and proved that yes, he *was* the strongest of them all. He re-holstered the laser gun, brushed plaster dust and splinters off his clothes, and strode off across the rubble toward Grid's place. As he left the wreckage of the Arena, Loki came up, drying his hands on a paper towel.

"Hey, when's the fight?" asked Loki innocently, "Have I missed anything?"

Thor was in too good a mood to beat Loki up, especially since he had to return the laser gun, power pack, etc. to Grid . . . and he should be able to get there just in time for supper. Loki breathed a deep sigh of relief . . . he'd escaped yet again! Living on the edge was dangerous . . . but man alive! It was *fun*!

And so, children, that is how Thor got his confidence and good spirits back. He was back in the saddle, as it were, and he vowed to himself to always have his hammer handy. Even in the shower. You never knew . . . .

Well, it's time for you to go to sleep. I hear your Mom coming to kiss you goodnight . . . I'll tell her that it was me who broke the pillow, OK? If she thinks that you did it, she won't let me come and tell you any more stories!

Chapter 13

THE DATING GAME

Well, children, it's bedtime again, which means that it's time for another story. We haven't heard much about Njord yet, so I'm going to tell you one about him tonight.

You both know that Njord lived all alone, except for a huge flock of seagulls who visited him every mealtime and when he was gutting fish or shucking clams for chowder. Seagulls aren't really much at conversation, though. Harbor seals are friendly enough, but they have their own agendas and don't bother Njord very much, unless Njord is gutting fish out in his dory. Both the seagulls and the seals *love* it when Njord goes fishing and gets a good haul.

Njord was sooooo lonely. The rest of the Æsir didn't visit much, though they did telephone. Njord was quite used to the sinus-clearing aroma clinging to his docks, shack, boats, clothes, and everything else in Njord's world. Long ago, his nose had simply quit registering that all-pervasive smell. Made it impossible to get a date, though. He simply didn't have a clue as to what was keeping everybody from coming down to see him. About the only god who came down to visit was Thor, but Njord didn't know that the thunder god's overriding purpose for those visits was to help Njord drink beer. Thor made sure that he emptied a keg or three before breathing deeply so that his nose would get numb and the smell didn't register as much. Once you got past the aroma, Njord was a really nice fellow with a great sense of humor and a good supply of new jokes. He was generous, and always sent really good birthday presents to everyone, and he made the finest clam chowder you could find in all the Worlds.

It wasn't long after Idunn's terrifying kidnapping . . . you kids remember that story, don't you? . . . that this all happened. Skadi, the only daughter of the late Thjazi, came home after graduating *cum laude* from prep school. Now, Thjazi had been a beer-swilling, football-loving blue-collar giant, but Skadi was ambitious and wanted to rise above that world. Her idea of the perfect husband was a professional type who lived in Greenwich, the type who went to Vail for the skiing and to Nantucket for the sailing. She had managed to purge that strong Jotun accent from her speech, and was very much at home in an LL Bjørn upscale world.

When Skadi came in the front door of her home, there was no blare of the TV to greet her, no growled "Hey! While yer on yer feet, bring me some more chips!", no Daddy. She dropped her bags in the middle of the living room floor and looked around. It didn't take a rocket scientist to see that it was obvious that her Daddy had left the place very suddenly, and that he hadn't returned home. He had obviously been gone for quite a while.

Skadi was a bit worried at this point. Daddy was tough, but he was getting on in years. His retirement pension after he left the Jotunheim Football Team (he'd been a fullback) kept them comfortable and paid Skadi's tuition, especially since Thjazi led a simple life. That big inheritance from Gramps hadn't hurt either. But Daddy had gotten a bit unpredictable of late. He'd always been a bit "different" after the skull fracture he'd gotten in that Dill Bowl game against the Muspellheim Marauders four years ago, but it wasn't like him to charge out of the house like that. Especially since the front door had been closed when Daddy had charged out.

Skadi picked up the worst of the debris, splinters of wood, and empty beer bottles. She then shooed out the various wildlife which had taken up residence in the house. Next, she tidied up and vacuumed the downstairs so that it would look halfway presentable. After that, she called Grizzlegutt & Sons, Carpenters, to come replace the shattered front door, emergency rush. Only after the new door was hung did Skadi finally get worried enough to start calling around to find out where Daddy had gone.

Nobody in Jotunheim had seen him. He hadn't gone to Muspellheim for a football party. It was as if he'd blasted out the door and vanished into thin air. Skadi realized that she'd have to bite the bullet and go ask Heimdall if the FBI could put a search out for him.

Meanwhile back at the docks, Njord made the big decision that he would really like to get married. He was already settled down, and he was certainly very well off, financially speaking. His business was very lucrative, and he had prospects of getting his chowders and fish products sold Worlds-wide in the Halt & Buy! Supermarket chain. He wasn't ugly . . . well, he was sort of *distinguished*-looking, in a nautical way. He thought he looked a lot like that Scottish actor Shaun Conneraigh, but in truth, he more

147

closely resembled the Gortainn Sea Foods man. I should be a good catch, he thought . . . I should go talk to Frey about how to reel in a good wife!

So Njord walked over to The Valhalla . . . it was a rather long haul, about five miles . . . in hopes of finding a wife. He was clueless about how to get a date, though he'd once heard that going to a bar should be the first move. The Einherjar, alerted by the advance wave of ripe long-dead fish odor, managed to keep Njord outside where there was a wind blowing. Njord explained his mission, and the Einherjar immediately (and to a man) told him that the first thing he needed was a really good hot long soaking bath. In fact, maybe a whole *series* of baths with an occasional sauna along the way. He would need all new clothes, too.

The Einherjar were quite happy to help a fellow man win the love of his life. Njord had a lot going for him, and if they could possibly get him decontaminated and fashionably dressed, maybe Njord could get lucky. The boys all remembered the fun they'd had getting Thor ready for that bridal trip to Jotunheim. Things had been getting a bit boring since then. There had been no missions for them to rally to, no excitement since that crazy Jotun Thjazi put the arm on Idunn and they nailed him coming over the Asgard Wall.

Suddenly the Einherjar had themselves a mission. The Valhalla's cooks started heating cauldrons of water, and someone ran over to The Golden Apple, Idunn's health food store, for a collection of herbal soaps guaranteed to remove bad odors, energize the skin, and provide work for native herb farmers in the rain forests of Southern Midgard. Frey came in partway through this process and tried to educate Njord in the ways of women and romance.

As I said, Njord was pretty clueless. Frey did his best, but in the end, it would have to be up to the old sea-dog himself. Shaking his head, Frey went out the door of The Valhalla. Balder was just coming in, probably for a lemonade. Frey got a sudden idea and took Balder to one side for a little conference.

"Look, Balder, I've tried to give Njord advice on how to get a date, but he's totally innocent when it comes to the ladies. You and I, between us, have had pretty good luck. Maybe we could think up something so that Njord wouldn't have to talk. He'd get all flustered and blow it if he talked to a girl. Could you imagine this? His idea of a good line is to say 'Hey, you busy? Maybe we could get married before the tide turns!' . . . can you *believe* that any guy could be so naïve?"

Balder, who always believed the best of anyone, said "Njord is a really nice fella. He's in *great* shape for someone his age, and I'm *sure* that we can find some way to help him! . . . . Hey! I just thought of something we could do! You know those ads I do? These companies would *really* like to sponsor a hit show, something in prime time! Maybe we could come up with a quiz show, some sort of game show . . . they're getting really popular right now!"

"I can see it now!" exclaimed Frey excitedly, "We could call the show 'Date a Millionaire!' That oughta bring women outta the *woodwork*! Njord's been doing really well and I'm sure that he has a *few* cool millions tucked away! He certainly doesn't spend anything much, and everybody buys his fish! His chowder can't be beat, either; I don't know of a single restaurant which doesn't buy from him! *He* could be our Mystery Millionaire!"

"Hey, I think we got a plan! I'll go bounce it off the big guys, while you see about rounding up a studio and film crew and also see if WASG-TV will carry it! Who knows, maybe we could get the networks interested . . . this could be big, BIG!"

And so it was. The station was *definitely* interested, which got Balder's ad agency interested, which got the sponsors interested . . . and before you knew it, other sponsors wanted "in", too. Balder and Frey had to scramble to get the show put together, props assembled, the set built, lighting, makeup, all that sort of stuff. Njord, meanwhile, was still in his makeover phase, and had about ten baths to go.

Heimdall made sure that this new show got good press. Front page, above the fold. It became the main topic of conversation in

every beauty parlor in all the nine Worlds. Nobody knew who the
Mystery Millionaire was, but since Mimir, the financial consultant
down at the Asgard Bank and Trust said that the fellow really *was*
a millionaire, would-be contestants started pouring into town.

Meanwhile, back in Jotunheim, Skadi changed into her Prep-
pie Corporate Look outfit. Dress for success, she'd been taught,
and success meant finding Daddy. Failing that, making sure that
she was the sole heiress to Daddy's nice pile of lovely money. She
trotted out to her BMW and headed for the Bifrost Memorial
Bridge. Heimdall saw her coming in plenty of time to put on his
badge and FBI baseball cap. When she entered his office, he was
ready.

"OK, miss, how can the FBI help you?"

"It's my Daddy. He's missing. I'd like to find him."

"Height? Age? Name? Occupation? Last known address?"

Children, the question and answer session went on for quite a
while. If I continued with that part, you'd be asleep before I got to
the end of the story. But finally Heimdall had to give Skadi the bad
news. He tried to soften it as best he could, but dead was dead.
Skadi had also found out that Loki was mixed up in this, of course,
as well as the Einherjar and a lot of the other gods. Heimdall, of
course, carefully did not mention any role he or the FBI might
have had in Thjazi's demise.

"Someone's gonna pay for this!" screamed Skadi as she left
Heimdall's office, slamming the door behind her. "I'm gonna hire
me the best lawyer in all the nine Worlds and I'm gonna sue Loki
and Odin and the rest of 'em so that they have to live on store-
brand catfood for the rest of their lives!"

The best lawyer around was Forseti, of course, but since he was always on the go, Skadi had to hunt up his father, Balder, who might know where Forseti was. Heimdall meanwhile put in a hurried phone call to Odin to give him a heads-up on the situation. Odin got to Balder first, and the three of 'em . . . Frey was still consulting with Balder . . . hatched up the idea to let Skadi become the first contestant on the new game show. Heimdall had reported that she wasn't married, and that she might just go for a wealthy suitor. And, if they managed to get her married to Njord, that would kill two birds with one stone. She'd be off their backs, and Njord would no longer be alone. Balder, Frey, and Odin were the only ones who knew who the Mystery Millionaire was, and they had somehow managed to keep it a total secret from everybody. They also made sure that the fact that they knew the Mystery Millionaire's identity remained a secret, too. Skadi would be so excited at being selected as the first contestant that she might forget all about this lawsuit stuff.

Well, that's not quite what happened. Skadi was pleased to get the first crack at a genuine millionaire businessman, but she insisted that *all* of the unmarried Æsir menfolk get into the lineup, too. She didn't really need the money, but getting a genuine Æsir husband sure beat getting a Jotun husband. Skadi tended to lump the Vanir and the Æsir together, so all of the single Vanir menfolk had to join the lineup. The first episode of this show was to be aired live, and was being picked up by the networks and beamed to all the Worlds via satellite.

Odin, of course, got to be the emcee. He was definitely married, so he didn't have to be a Mystery Millionaire. The rules of the show were that all of the eligible men . . . there were several . . . had to be hidden behind a curtain, with only their bare feet showing. Heimdall (who was unmarried and also behind the curtain) had arranged for voice-distortion instrumentation so that the contestant (Skadi) couldn't pick out someone by voice alone.

Loki could disguise his voice, but the other men weren't as talented. Odin also interpreted the "millionaire" requirement a bit loosely so that Loki could be tossed into the pool. Loki was certainly good for a million laughs. Would serve him right to be married off on the spot to a pushy Jotun valley girl! Odin grinned wickedly at the thought.

The day of the broadcast dawned bright and fair. The show was being filmed in the Opera House, since that facility had all kinds of elaborate stage sets and comfortable auditorium seating. Odin got dressed in a natty suit with a red carnation in the buttonhole. Mimir, as the verifying accountant, was his usual nervous rumpled self, overstuffed briefcase and all. Skadi donned a peach and beige Land's Beginning outfit, peach colored low-heeled pumps by Bassi, and a pale green scarf by Herm of Normandy. Her hair was styled by Vidarr Sassoonsson, her perfume by Kristjan Djur, and her accessories supplied by Saxon Fifthstreet. Dr. Skoal's Foot Powder was also a sponsor, thanks to the display of bare feet.

The Mystery Millionaires were brought to the Green Room backstage in absolute secrecy. Heimdall had commandeered his own surveillance van with one-way windows for the transportation end of things, and he also had agents keeping folks well clear of the stage entrance. Odin's wolves helped the agents on the ground, and the ravens kept Odin informed on progress backstage. The hall filled rapidly, and soon it was standing room only. It was showtime!

Just as the sundial read noon, the orchestra in the pit swung into action. The conductor had picked the brassiest thing he could think of offhand, which was the Triumphal March from "Aieeeeeee! Guhhh!", an opera about romance, treachery, and death in some country down south a long time ago. As the orchestra reached the crashing finale of the piece, the house lights dimmed, the gold curtain rose, and Odin entered stage left. The audience applauded wildly on cue as Odin took his place at the podium with Mimir at his side. At stage right, there was a long booth with a red velvet curtain in front which had a gap of about one foot between its fringed bottom and the floor.

As the applause crested and died down, a jolly stentorian voice crisply announced "It's Tiiiiime To Daaate a Mmmmillllionnnaaaiiiirrrrrreee! But first, these words from our sponsors!" Odin rustled some papers and held a quick confab with Mimir while the commercials rolled, and then when the red "on the air" light winked on again, he straightened up, smiled at the camera, and announced the rules of the game. Then the stentorian voice announced "Annnnd nowww for ourrr firrrst contessstant, Misss Skadiiii Thjazzzisdottirrrr!" and Skadi strode out to her podium with a confident expression. All the Worlds were watching her, and she wanted to make a good impression. And then, on cue, a whole row of bare feet shuffled up to the Millionaire's Booth curtain from behind, with their owners completely hidden from view. Odin had also been careful to enchant the entire booth so that those gods with x-ray vision or ESP couldn't tell who was inside it, either.

"Well, Miss Thjazisdottir, you have in front of you eight possibilities for wedded bliss! Each one is guaranteed to be a millionaire," Odin lied glibly . . . Loki was back there, and although it's true that he'd had a lot of money during his lifetime so far, it was also true that he'd spent far more than that and was in debt up to his ears, as usual. But he *was* worth a million laughs, so Odin figured he'd be safe if Skadi happened to pick him. The others had similar "millionaire" qualifications in something other than money, too. Odin continued: "Each one is single, and the one you pick is yours to marry on the spot! Thor is standing by with his hammer to hallow the bride and groom, and we've arranged for a three-week honeymoon, all expenses paid, in sunny Denmark!"

Applause. A few wolf-whistles. Skadi preened herself and glowed with anticipation. She *knew* that Balder would be back there, and he was drop-dead handsome. He was good and kind and extremely popular. If she could identify *his* feet, now . . . . What Skadi didn't know was that Balder's wife was still around. Nobody saw much of Nanna, so Skadi could be excused for her ignorance. That left Njord, of course, as well as Loki, Skirnir, Heimdall, Hod, Tyr, Hoenir, and Ullr. Mimir was excused, since he was advising Odin. Skadi could ask each millionaire one question, and each millionaire was under a bombproof geas to give a truthful answer. Loki was squirming uncomfortably behind the screen as this rule was explained, but he was also under another geas to remain in place and not skip out before the final choice was made. Skirnir was upset, too, but Hod, Hoenir, Tyr, and Ullr were perfectly happy to get a chance to get married. Heimdall wouldn't have minded getting married in order to get a good housekeeper and cook, but the security risk . . . and her a Jotun . . . he was not happy with his chances.

Skadi surveyed the row of feet. The first pair was flat as a pancake, with gnarly toes. The second pair was wrinkled and frog-belly white. The third pair was a possibility; they were tanned and muscular. Hmmmmm . . . the fourth pair was scrawny and looked as if they had some sort of fungus. The fifth pair looked as if the owner kicked cinderblocks for a hobby; they were sturdy, wide, thick . . . musta been size 22EEE. Number six had toenail polish on . . . an attractive shade, too. Skadi made a mental note to ask the owner of those feet what brand that polish was; it would go well with her dusty rose Pendelsson wool pants-suit. The sev-

155

enth pair was flat and had bunions, which wouldn't do at all. The last pair of feet was beautiful. A high arch, well-manicured nails, beautifully straight toes, and a pale blond-ish fuzz over the ankles. Skadi mentally narrowed her choice down to Suitor Number Three and Suitor Number Eight.

"Suitor Number Three, what is your favorite hobby?"

"Skiing, mostly," came back the disguised answer. "I also like fishing, hunting, and living in the country."

Hmmmmmm . . . .Skiing is certainly good, Skadi mused to herself . . . and fishing and hunting too . . . must belong to a country club. He must also have a country estate . . . *definitely* a possibility!

"Suitor Number Eight, what is your favorite hobby?"

"Hobby? Um, fishing, I guess," came the hesitant answer, "mostly I'm at work, though."

Aha. A professional man, must be a surgeon or a lawyer or . . . yes, Balder works a lot! Didn't know he was into fishing, but you never know . . . he *does* seem to have an affinity for water. And those feet . . . they're *gorgeous*! Skadi wasn't quite drooling, but as she gazed at those feet, she became more and more sure in her mind that they could *only* belong to Balder.

"OK, I am picking Suitor Number Eight!" she declared triumphantly. Wouldn't her Jotunheim neighbors be jealous green when they saw who *she'd* snagged for a husband! Skadi grinned from ear to ear in happy anticipation as Thor entered from the wings with Mjollnir in his left hand, its handle tied with long white ribbons which trailed on the ground behind the god. In his right hand, Thor held a small box containing two golden wedding rings.

Odin smiled at the cameras and then said "Are you absolutely sure?" and Skadi nodded yes . . . she was so excited that she could hardly speak . . . and the Odin said "Very well . . . we shall find out who Suitor Number Eight is right *after* station identification and these messages from our sponsors!" and then the red "on the air" light blinked off. "We have three minutes here", continued Odin, "the sponsors wanted all their ads at this point in the game, since the audience should be glued to the screen waiting to see who the Mystery Millionaire is!"

The band played some incidental music suitable for Midsummer Night, and then got out the sheet music for the Wedding March from "The Swan Knight". The suitors behind the curtain weren't absolutely sure who was what number, so there was more than a little nervous (disguised) chatter there; fortunately, the mikes were dead so they didn't pick up Loki's whining. It seemed forever before the red "on the air" light flashed on again and Odin waved grandly at the Millionaires' Booth.

"Behind that curtain are eight unmarried gods," said Odin grandly, "But only *one* will speak the wedding vows in front of you, the audience and the television viewers of the Nine Worlds! I will call out the numbers of the runners-up, who will be taken backstage by my staff (here, the wolves and ravens snapped to and looked alert) . . . the seventh runner up is . . . Hod!" The gnarly flat feet moved out of sight and Skadi breathed a sigh of relief . . . migawwd! I coulda picked Hod! "Annd now for runner-up number six . . . Loki!" The scrawny feet moved out of sight. Skadi gasped; how did Loki qualify??? And thank heavens I didn't pick *him*! EEEeewwww!

Six pairs of feet remained. "The fifth runner up is . . . Tyr!" proclaimed Odin, and the pallid wrinkled feet backed away out

of sight. Skadi was surprised that the old warhorse had partici-
pated in this kind of event . . . but he *was* famous for his honor
and courage. "Runner-up number four is . . . Heimdall!" The fuzz!
Skadi would have had a heckuva time living that down, being
married to the head Fed . . . "And runner up number three is
Skirnir!" The owner of those feet obviously fainted at that point,
because suddenly his feet flipped up so that the soles were pointing out at the audience, and then the feet vanished as if someone
was dragging their owner offstage. "Runner up Number Two is . . .
Hoenir!" The very large, tough-looking feet came to attention and
then backed off out of sight. "And the last runner up is . . . Ullr!"
Skadi sighed as the tanned, athletic feet vanished. She had nearly
picked them, too! Ullr was a penniless ski bum who lived in a
tarpaper shack out in the boonies! She shuddered delicately. What
kind of secret inheritance does *he* have to qualify as a Mystery
Millionaire? she wondered.

"A drum-roll, please!" said Odin pompously. "It is time for
the winning suitor, the Mystery Millionaire, the Groom For Today
to be revealed!" The snare drums began a pianissimo roll which
crescendoed gradually through piano, mezzo, mezzo forte, forte,
fortissimo, and fortississsiisssimo. The wolves stood at attention
on either side of the booth, while the ravens pulled on the cord
holding the curtain up. The red velvet curtain fell, puddling at the
feet of Njord who was dressed in a white tuxedo. His hair and
beard had been expertly trimmed, and his broad smile gleamed as
he raised his arms in triumph.

Children, Njord was a god transformed. The rest of the Æsir
and Vanir stared at him . . . why, he was *handsome*!!! His dark
beard and hair were dramatically streaked with silver, and he stood
straight and tall as he came forward to claim his bride.

Skadi couldn't believe her eyes. She'd been fixated on getting Balder . . . and she'd gotten *Njord*!!! But then . . . (here, Thor

raised his hammer to hallow the bridal couple as the sea-god gently took one of Skadi's hands in his) . . . then . . . well, Njord isn't *that* bad looking . . . he's actually quite distinguished, in fact . . . he owns quite a fleet of ships and he *is* highly respected . . . Hmmmm . . . either it's him or I go back to Jotunheim with my tail between my legs to face all my friends' laughter and jokes . . . .

At this point, Odin asked each one if he or she would marry the other, in sickness and in health, etc., and Njord said "I do" in sort of a hushed awed voice . . . Skadi was really *beautiful* for a Jotun . . . and then Skadi said "I do" and then a sort of St. Elmo's Fire glowed around Mjollnir and the bridal couple and then the orchestra started in on the Swan Knight piece fortissimo and all the ladies in the audience started crying and throwing confetti.

Children, that was quite a wedding! I wish I could tell you that they lived happily ever after, but just after the honeymoon ended, Njord took Skadi back to his home by the docks. She managed to stick it out for a week, but then the fish smell, screaming gulls, and salt on everything got to be too much. Njord, the gentle, ever-courteous, generous sea-god, then agreed to go up into the mountains with her to the darling little ski chalet she'd bought with her graduation money. He tried his level best to like it, but after about a week, the cold, frostbite, and altitude sickness got to him, and he dizzily and sadly had to explain that he couldn't live there full-time. They then struck a deal that they'd alternate weeks at each place. After a while, Skadi and Njord decided that maybe they'd live for three weeks alone in their own place and then on the fourth week visit the spouse, alternating from the ski lodge to the docks.

I suppose that it's just good for Njord's peace of mind that he never did find out that during the separation time, Skadi began having an affair with Ullr, Suitor Number Three, whose tanned athletic feet she'd almost picked. But that's another story, and it's time now for you to close your eyes and drift off to sleep.

Chapter 14

HOW BALDER BOUGHT THE FARM

Uncle Einar has another story for you, children, and since it's almost Hallowe'en, this one is good and spooky. It's about Balder, who was one of the nicest fellows in all Asgard, and how he was involved in a certain real estate deal. Loki's in it, too, this time up to the ears. Actually, just about everyone shows up.

Once upon a time on a dark and stormy night, the Norn sisters all had exactly the same dream. It was a lulu, let me tell you! A coal-black Nightmare with fangs delivered it, special delivery, straight from Muspellheim Dreamworks, Unlimited. That establishment, shrouded in corporate secrecy, sends good dreams via white and pastel-colored Daymares, as well as some real stemwinders carried by your common, ordinary grey and midnight-blue Nightmares. The totally blood-curdling, turn-your-hair-white screamers get shipped out with the black Nightmares. This particular dream got special treatment, since its Nightmare had unusually long canine teeth and a huge set of bat wings. As I've said before, Asgard isn't your usual suburban town. And a "people" nightmare here on Earth is tame compared to one designed for the gods in Asgard.

This particular dream was so violently dramatic with the usual falling/firestorm/fear overtones, that the Norns as one suddenly woke up, sitting bolt upright in their beds with cold sweat rolling down their faces. The pepperoni-jalapeño-sardine pizzas they'd had for dinner may possibly have contributed to this simultaneous vision, but the Norns realized that there was far more to this than simple heartburn. As one, they tossed off their clammy bedclothes and raced to their library. There was an urgent, yea, desperate consultation among the sisters, each backing up her viewpoint with quotes from her favorite texts. Interpreting a True Dream was tricky, and had to be done right.

A few hours later as dawn tiptoed across the morning sky, the Norns finally agreed as to what their dream meant. Balder was doomed to die unless the gods got everything in all the Worlds to swear cross-their-hearts not to harm him in any way. Now, *everyone* liked Balder. He didn't have a mean bone in his body, and was the good example that all Asgardian kids were told to be like. The bad example was always Loki. Now, if *he* bit the big one, nobody'd grieve. But Balder??!!??

Urd dashed down to The Valhalla with the news. Verdandi covered the Asgard Ladies' Guild, which had the best grapevine known to god or man. Skuld hot-footed it to Heimdall with a flash release for the *Gjallarhorn Gazette*. And before you could say the word "Superoptikjempefantofenomenalistisk!", everyone and everything knew what the Norns' prediction said. In Asgard, trees and rocks and worms and such were just as awake as people and dogs and cats are here. Also, the Norns were *never* wrong . . . .

Nanna, Balder's wife, went into hysterics at the news. Balder, bless him, was on location filming a Perrier ad, and since he could only hold one thought in his mind at a time, the news didn't bother him at all. The cameras were rolling, and he was "on". Frigg, who faithfully followed the Norns' astrology column in the *Gazette*, got every single female in Asgard to go around and get everything in all the Worlds to promise not to harm Balder in any way. Odin rallied the Einherjar and the rest of the boys. His staff (Hugin, Munin, Geri and Freki) got all of the birds and land animals to promise not to hurt Balder. Aegir and Ran asked the whales and porpoises to get promises from everything that lived in the sea. Idunn and Bragi took care of the plant, bug, bacterial, viral, and yeast kingdoms, but somehow they missed mistletoe.

Now, if you've ever seen it, mistletoe is one of the weaker, scrawnier, more shiftless plants going. It even mooches off other trees, so's not to have to go to the bother of making roots! But mistletoe has an incredible amount of white magic tied up in it, so I guess Idunn thought that of *course* mistletoe wouldn't hurt Balder. Anyway, by about noontime the Aesir and Vanir were finally satisfied that Balder was safe, and that the Norns' prediction would not come to pass.

But they hadn't reckoned with Loki. Loki was down in Utgard-Loki's Pool Hall cheating at blackjack, and he was feeling his oats. So far, nobody'd caught him yet today. When he heard about the Norns' prediction, he sniggered and fingered the wad of bills in his pocket. Balder had lectured Loki many times on Clean Living, and Loki was sick and tired of hearing the same lecture over and over and over. It was payback time.

Before long, Loki'd also found out about the mistletoe. So he strolled over to Igor the Friendly Arms Merchant's warehouse and parted with most of his cash for the latest, best thing in a missile, TOW (tube-operated, optically-guided, wire-controlled). Loki was playing for keeps this time.

163

Children, I don't know *why* the gods tempted Fate. When Balder had finished the day's filming, he went straight to The Valhalla for a lemonade and a ride on the bucking bull. And the Einherjar, who were pretty well oiled by then, started chucking empties at him and were laughing uproariously when each bottle veered sharply away from Balder just before it would have struck him. Pickled eggs and cigar butts did the same thing. Pretty soon, everyone got into the act. Balder, unhurt and unmussed, rode serenely on, waving his Hopalong Cassidy hat and singing "Whoopie, Ti-yi Yo, Get Along Little Dogies!" at the top of his lyrically beautiful tenor voice. Freyja, mesmerized, blew him kiss after kiss. And folks were throwing everything they could think of (including the kitchen sink) at Balder and screaming and laughing as their missiles missed.

Everyone was having such a good time that they didn't notice Loki slink up to the back of the crowd. And Loki, who was one of the best shape-changers in Asgard, had disguised his armament to look like a bunch of wilted lettuce. He noticed blind Hod, who was doing a land-office business in swizzle sticks, Mylar souvenir balloons, pink fuzzy stuffed animals on sticks, and suchlike. Hod was a perfect patsy, thought Loki as he suggested that Hod join in the fun, too.

"Hey, I'm visually challenged!" objected Hod, "And damned if I throw away perfectly good merchandise that I can get a coupla bucks for!"

"Awww, c'mon, be a sport! Everyone is throwing stuff! Here, I got something for you to lob, and it won't cost you a penny!"

"But there's so much noise that I don't know which direction to throw anything! And if I *do* happen to aim at someone else, they could get hurt!"

"Heyyy, no sweat! I'll just guide your hands," smirked Loki as he quickly and completely wiped his fingerprints off the "lettuce". "OK, Hod, let 'er rip!"

Hod, wanting to be just like the Einherjar, let 'er rip. Kablooie! He was startled that lettuce would make a sound like that, and he was stunned to hear only dead silence (aside from something slowly dripping) when the echoes of the blast had faded. Loki, of course, had quickly faded from the scene.

Freyja screamed and fainted, covered in reddish goo. The bucking bull, untouched, bucked on, but nobody rode him now. The smell of rocket propellant and gore filled the air. Balder was all over the place. Everyone else just stared, numbly, at the carnage.

Hela discreetly took care of the worst of it with a mop and a bucket. She was a professional, and quickly and competently went about her task. It wasn't easy being a mortician in a land inhabited by gods and immortals, so the rare death was a major event in her life. Odin shakily opened the bar to all, on the house, while Frigg went to see Nanna. After all, Balder was Odin's and her son, and Frigg needed a good cry with Balder's wife. Hugin and Munin were dispatched to find Forseti, and Geri and Freki volunteered to howl at the funeral along with Garm.

Before long, Hela had Balder (or all she could find of him) in her fanciest rosewood-and-ebony coffin, Model RIP 4FR, the one with the gold handles studded with diamonds. The mourning room was set up, and black bunting draped everywhere. The guest book for (closed coffin) viewing was open on a basalt stand, and Garm was fitted with his black mourning collar. As she had nobody to run the souvenir shop, she had to keep her eye on that, too. The tab on this one would be enough to keep her going for ten years, she calculated, as she totted up the expenses for the shroud, mop, bucket, sponges, special expenses, dealer prep charges, delivery costs, etc. Hela was a shrewd businesswoman, and loaded everything she could think of onto the bill. And after all, everybody was in such a state of shock and grief that they certainly wouldn't notice a *tiny* little decimal point moved three places to the right.

Being a goddess, Hela was able to magic up a three-dimensional holograph of Balder just as he was in life. She added audio as well, so folks could talk to the dear departed. The dry-ice fog that billowed across the midnight-black floor was from a machine, however, and was billable at a mere $75/hour. Hela also made sure that the front door creaked eerily, the bats were on duty, and that there were plenty of cobwebs draped all over everything. Coffin-shaped dark Godiva chocolates were arranged on a Victorian mourning platter, and Garm began to howl. It was a thoroughly spooky scene, you betcha! Hela was doing this one up brown.

Just as arrangements were nearing completion, Urd came in with an Urgent Message from her crystal ball. If everyone and everything grieved for Balder, he would be magically restored to life. Hela was hesitant at first, but cheered up when Odin reached for the bill and paid it in cash, in full, on the spot, with a 20% tip included. Again the news went out, and all things set in to grieving. Those that were within earshot of Garm, Geri, and Freki really wept and moaned. Garm had that effect on folks. And rocks. And trees. Etc.

It was one heckuva funeral, let me tell you! Complete with burning Viking ship sent off into the sunset (deluxe ship pyre, $800,000; environmental-impact statement and associated fees, $1,400; Union fire crew from Muspellheim, $250,000; burning permit issued by the town of Asgard, $25). Heimdall and his deputies began investigating what had happened. And all things grieved for Balder.

Well, actually, not *quite* all things grieved for Balder. Loki, disguised as a chambermaid at Utgard-Loki's place until the heat was over, only pretended. Oh, the tears were real, all right, but that was because Loki was laughing so hard. So Balder remained only a hologram, never to leave the Hell-Hole Funeral Home. Actually, Hela was relieved that he stayed dead, too; now she had someone to run the souvenir stand and to sell popcorn to the kiddies. It would have been really disconcerting if every time you got a body, arranged the funeral, and billed the family, the dear departed came back to life. Of course, there'd be some repeat business, mused Hela . . . .

So that is how Balder bought the farm, and why Heimdall is looking high and low for Loki. This is also why Freyja doesn't seem interested in coming down to the Valhalla much anymore, and why Odin looks a lot grimmer than he did before. Thor and Mjollnir would purely love to weigh in, too.

I realize that this story wasn't all sweetness and light, but life's like that. And Balder, though kind of transparent-looking now, can still think and talk and act . . . and his reviewers say that his advertising work has taken on an ethereal, spirited touch which would surely deserve a Clio the next time around.

It's time to go to sleep, now, children . . . oh, are you worried about the Nightmare? All right, I'll leave a night-light on. Nightmares don't like light very much. And here's your teddy bears and your blankies. I'll be just around the corner, so sleep tight!

168

Chapter 15

LOKI LIPS OFF

Well, hullo, there, children! Your Dad and Mom tell me that you both got A's on your science projects! Well done! Sure is a nice change, isn't it? Well, I have an extra-special story for you tonight that I've saved for just such an occasion as this. You all like hearing about Loki, don't you? Well, he's up to his usual tricks again.

Actually, the story properly begins with Ægir and Ran. That's Dr. Ægir Hlersson and Dr. Ran Jotunsdottir. I haven't told you much about them so far, mostly because they're usually busy in their underwater oceanographic research station and rarely mix with the "flatlanders" of Asgard. Oh, they send email all over the place and belong to chat groups, especially ones dealing with marine science, but they essentially live in their little world and don't bother anyone. To tell the truth, they are usually so busy with their sample-taking, salinity and current readings, plankton surveys, sea-floor core readings and whatnot that the ordinary goings-on in Asgard aren't really very interesting to them. Folks have to go out to their place if they want to see them in person. Most of the folks who visit them are fellow scientists, though the occasional blue-water sailor does drop in now and then.

Well, children, one day Ægir got The Big Phone Call From Stockholm. Something about his work on plate tectonics, the rift in the floor of the Great Salty Sea, unusual anaerobic life-forms therein, and a lot of other really technical stuff that had revolutionized marine science. Ran started screaming with joy and running around the station, which was a pretty big installation. After all, besides the labs, computer room, storage areas, deep-sea exploration vehicle "hangar" and the observation deck, there were living quarters for the Hlersson family (ten bedrooms . . . each of their nine daughters *insisted* on her own room), a huge geodesic dining/living room with a great view of the sea floor around the station, gourmet kitchen, guest rooms for visiting scientists, library, well, the list goes on. The Hlerssons were living in a facility which would have made the folks at Woods Hole Oceanographic Institute jealous green.

Ægir tried to get some more work done. He had a journal article to finish; the editor had been bugging him about deadlines, and the final deadline was that day. It was hard for him to concentrate, though, what with the swelling numbers of congratulatory phone calls and emails, and then his daughters all coming in from their various research sites, and Ran calling up folks to invite them to a big party that night to celebrate. Finally, Ægir disappeared into the computer room, locked the door, and tried to finish his manuscript. He put a CD in the player, "Death-Punk Screamin' Blues!" by the Valkyries, and cranked up the volume to drown out the pounding on the door.

About two and a half hours later he emerged, having finally faxed his finished article to the journal. He was met by a scene of utter pandemonium. The girls were rushing about picking up the place, vacuuming, putting out dishes of chips and peanuts, and hiding stacks and reams of research notes. Ran was busy in the kitchen. It was evident that the Hlerssons were going to have what seemed to be everybody in Asgard coming to the "Congratulations!" party that night. Ran had made pans and pans of lasagna and piles of loaves of fresh-baked garlic bread . . . the good kind that screams "GARRLIC!" at the top of its lungs. There were steamship rounds of beef, huge hams, lobster newburg, a vat of Njord's clam chowder, poached salmon, salads of all kinds, and desserts of even more kinds. Ægir had never seen so much food in one place in his life. But when a hotel management Ph.D. like Ran got a good excuse to put on a killer party, all Ægir could do was to quickly retreat into the library and pick up a thriller involving manganese nodule formation in the abyssal environment . . . yes, children, that *is* a mouthful, but that was Ægir's idea of light reading.

Before he'd gotten very far into his book, the doorbell rang. To his delight, it was his favorite band, the Valkyries, who were going to perform gratis for the occasion. They commandeered one of the girls' bedrooms to use as a Green Room, and started setting up their equipment. The next folks in were Odin and Frigg, and pretty soon the doorbell was ringing almost constantly. Since the guests were all gods, they could breathe underwater just fine, and had no problems coming in the front door without letting any water in. Thjalfi and Roskva, Thor's assistants, had magical pendants which allowed them to breathe underwater, so they could come, too. They told Ran that Thor and Sif would be late; they were on a Harley Owners' Toy Run to benefit the fatherless children of unsuccessful Vikings.

It was good that Ran arranged for two bartenders to help out. Their job was easy in that all the guests wanted to drink were mead, ale, and beer, but their job was difficult in that the Hlerssons were home brewers and had easily fifty kinds of each beverage on hand. Ran instructed the bartenders to serve Loki only Shirley Temples. Loki was no fun at all when he was passed out.

Folks started getting cheerier and cheerier as they got into the beer, ale and mead. The food was fabulous, and everybody was having a whee of a time. Njord did his codfish imitations, Frey his barnyard imitations, and Freyja was hastily stopped from giving *her* imitations. There were children present, and that sort of thing was strictly R rated. Tyr recited "The Battle of Malden" with sound effects, and Odin (in a professional capacity) sampled every single ale, beer, and mead that was available. His favorites were Davy Jones' Lager, Mushroom Madness Mead, Ol' Skull 'n' Crossbones Ale, and Sunk Without A Trace Lambic Ale. He was just about to talk to Ægir about stocking these at The Valhalla when Loki started in on one of his tirades.

Loki had somehow managed to get his hands on a temporarily abandoned horn of Shipwrecked Ale. That meant that Loki soon lost all of his manners and started whining and complaining and kvetching and moaning about Life, Life's Indignities, and Loki's Lousy Lot in Life. That led to one of the bartenders snatching the half-emptied horn out of Loki's hands, and then Loki going after the bartender with a steak knife. And *that* led to the Valkyries grabbing Loki by the scruff of his neck and tossing him out the front door, hoping that a great white shark would get him.

Before long, Loki was back. He was hopping mad, and started lipping off to the first person he met. That unfortunate soul was the second bartender, who got the worst tongue-lashing of his life. As the bartender escaped to complain to Ran about this, Loki swaggered into the center of the oversized living/dining room area. He looked around with a sneer on his lips, and demanded a horn of the best. After all, everybody else was drinking, so why was everybody dumping on Loki, forcing him to drink kiddie drinks?

Yes, children, *I* know that kiddie drinks are delicious. But Loki wanted to be a two-fisted he-man like the other fellas, which meant that swigging a chocolate milkshake was straight out. Not the macho thing. And since Ægir didn't brew O'Doolie's Alcohol-Free "Beer" Drink, all there was on hand was pretty high octane. Ran did *not* want Loki ruining her party, but the poor misguided soul thought that by *denying* Loki a real beer, he would calm down. Had she poured him a horn of "Badass Berserker", Loki woulda folded up like a Chinese fan and slept soundly and quietly for the rest of the night.

Hindsight is a wonderful thing. But at that moment, Bragi, who was Idunn's husband and also a home brewer, tried to shush Loki and get him off to the sidelines. Loki was having none of it. He was totally out of control and could care less, about things. All the venom and jealousy he'd stored since he was a rug-rat in Jotunheim came spilling out. And poor Bragi was at ground zero.

"Don't *you* try shushing me up, Bragi! I'm here, whether you like it or not, and I want my say!"

"Loki, you've had a hard day. Why don't you go lie down and have a little snooze? As you are, you're not fit company for a celebration party! It's Ægir's day! Let *him* bask in the limelight!"

"Like (children, here Loki uses words you don't know . . . no, I'm *not* going to tell you what words. Besides, they're in Old Norse, Old Saxon, Old Gothic, or Old Gaulish.)", screamed Loki, "You (again, children, I shall spare you the details, but the upshot was that Loki did not wish to leave the party, and thought that Bragi was an old fuddy-duddy)!!!"

"Look, Loki, I think it'd be best if you left the party. Now."

"Hey, Odin! Remember how you adopted me as your blood relative? You promised that if you partied, I would party!"

Odin, ruing the day he'd adopted Loki, agreed that Loki had a point. Remember, folks took family ties, biological or adopted, *very* seriously back then. Which meant that Odin grabbed a horn, filled it from the nearest bottle, and handed it to Loki. I think he was hoping that Loki would chug it, pass out, and cease to be a problem. No such luck. Loki was on a roll.

"Skoal, everybody! Everybody, that is, except Bragi there, who is such a (um, children, right here he referred to a part of a horse's anatomy. Which part? Um . . . er, its *tail*! Why? Oh, that's just because one of Loki's children was a horse . . . yes, heh heh heh, *that's* it . . .)!!"

"Look, Loki, you're not feeling good. I can loan you a horse so's you can get home and sleep it off. Deal?" Bragi hopefully also offered Loki a coupla bucks in case he got lost or needed to make a phone call.

"Bragi, you're broke, you and I know it, and any horse you have is in your dreams! Hey, ya wanna fight? Naah, you're chicken! You know it and I know it! And now *everybody* knows it!"

Idunn put out one hand just in time to stop Bragi from getting up, stomping over to Loki, and pounding him flat. She reminded him that they were pacifists, and that fighting was not the way to attain peace on earth. Loki laughed raucously as Bragi sheepishly agreed with his wife. He the proceeded to insult Idunn (called her a tart), Gefjon who was visiting from Copenhagen (called her a tart), Odin (but Odin called Loki a tart), Frigg (I don't know why Loki kept calling all the women tarts; but he also accused Frigg of being a tart) . . .what's that, children? Oh, a tart is a kind of pie. Right. Pie.

Loki worked his way through every single guest there, insulting them, calling them names, and in general doing his best to wreck Ægir's party. Ægir was getting a little hot on the collar at that point, and Heimdall was looking grim as he got out his handcuffs and stun gun. It was only when Beyla, Byggvir's wife . . . oh, remember Byggvir? He runs Frey's farm. Well, Beyla, who was looking out the window at the sea anemone garden, suddenly announced that Thor and Sif were coming. She then skittered over to the front door to fill them in on the goings-on. Thor, who had been well-pleased with the results of the Toy Run, was *not* pleased to hear about Loki. He could hear Loki's strident, nasal whine above the growling of the other guests. Ran was huddled in the kitchen, crying in great choking sobs because her beautiful party was ruined.

That was enough for Thor. Loki was monopolizing the whole evening, and Thor was not going to stand for it. He strode in with his hammer in his hand, to be met with a stream of nasty language and insults. The thunder god was now in no mood to take any guff, so he reached for Loki with his free hand. Loki snarled back at him as he skipped out of range.

"Some party this is, you gutless wonders! Don't be surprised if some day real soon this place just happens to burn to the ground!" And with that, Loki slipped out the front door and was gone. Thor was mad that he didn't get to beat Loki up. Heimdall quietly announced that this was it, that Loki was going onto the "Ten Most Wanted" list with a list of charges from which even Forseti, had he wanted to, could get Loki acquitted. Heimdall had a *very* large file on Loki, and this time the little weasel had gone too far.

Ægir sat there glumly and silently among a roomful of silent, glum guests. Then suddenly, he started to grin, then smile, then burst out in laughter. He laughed so hard that tears rolled down his cheeks. Ran scooted out of the kitchen to see what was so funny. When he could speak again, Ægir asked everyone how Loki thought he could torch a building which was *under water*.

One, then another, then the whole roomful had a good laugh at Loki's expense. The bartenders got busy, and the party finally got going again. But in the back of everyone's mind was the niggling thought that Loki had finally flipped out, and that something really bad was going to happen. Heimdall slipped out of the room with his "mission face" on, and Thor quietly followed him. Odin, having finally learned that it was Loki who had really been responsible for Balder's death, authorized any and all measures for Loki's capture. He deputized Tyr and Hoenir, who recruited the Einherjar. Heimdall had the APB out on all broadcast and print media within the hour, but Loki seemed to have vanished from the Worlds.

There were no more problems between then and the award ceremony in Stockholm. Ægir got his medallion and prize money, and had his picture in all the papers. All Asgard was thrilled that one of their own had achieved such a high honor. And the search went on for Loki. The gods could be very patient, like a cat at a mousehole. Heimdall managed to get an agent in place at Utgard-Loki's Pool Hall, just in case Loki showed up there. But it was as if the little punk had never existed.

Sif was convinced that Loki was planning something really spectacular. She knew that the little twerp wanted to be Mr. Big. Something about compensation for a weedy physique and a sub-beta standing in society. Thor was worried because Sif was worried, which meant that the Asgard chapter of Hell's Angels went on a round-the-sundial patrol. Odin was livid with anger that Loki, whom he'd trusted (sort of) and welcomed as family, had been responsible for Balder's murder. He forgave Hod, who had told Heimdall and Odin everything. Odin simply wanted Loki's guts for garters. Everybody in Asgard was looking for Loki, and Tyr and Thor made sure that "Old Sparky" . . . that's the electric chair, children . . . was in good repair and ready to go.

Well, that's all I have for tonight. Tomorrow night I'll tell you the story about the manhunt for Loki. It's a real humdinger, you betcha.

Chapter 16

LOKI'S TERRIBLE DAY

Children, it's been a loooonnng day, and your Uncle Einar is pooped. But I simply *have* to tell you this story to-night, especially since you were so nice to the cop who pulled us over for doing 60 in a 35-mph. zone. This story is about cops, too, sort of.

You remember how Loki was always getting into trouble? No, *not* like your Uncle Einar! I just make a lot of honest mis-takes! Loki *meant* what he was doing. Different thing entirely! Well, after the mess he made of Ægir's big party and Odin finding out who'd supplied the missile (TOW) and gotten Hod to fire it at Balder, Loki was at the top of Heimdall's list. Odin told Heimdall, Tyr, the Einherjar, heck, *everybody* in Asgard and Vanaheim that he wanted Loki caught, prosecuted, and condemned to life in prison without the remotest chance of parole. No rules for cap-ture, which meant that any means could be used up to and includ-ing tactical nukes. Loki knew Miranda by heart, so no need to repeat that to him, either. Odin and Frigg, along with Forseti and Nanna, put up a humongous reward on Loki's head. Forseti was doing *very* well as a lawyer, so the reward was enough to make

178

even Odin drool. Forseti also wanted to be the prosecuting attorney on this one. He wouldn't even charge for his services if he got a chance to put Loki away.

Heimdall, Odin and Tyr put their heads together. Loki was one heckuva clever, slippery character, yah shure! He had too many friends in unsavory neighborhoods, too many bolt-holes to hide in. Thor came in partway through the meeting to get a keg of Bad Goat! Doppelbock Beer and wound up staying there in The Valhalla while everybody tried to figure out how to put the arm on Loki. Thor mentioned that he could get the Asgard chapter of Hell's Angels into the act. He also suggested that the Valkyries might be able to help out, as they played some mighty rough gigs.

Before long, almost all of the Æsir and Vanir were huddled in the main bar-room of The Valhalla. Odin supplied free drinks and nachos to all, as the meeting looked as if it were going to be an all-nighter. About the only ones who didn't show up were Bragi and Idunn, who were agonizing over whether to protest this kangaroo court or not. Dedicated pacifists, they *still* thought that maybe Loki could be rehabilitated. But they were definitely in the minority, opinion-wise.

The upshot of the meeting was that Loki first had to be located. Search parties were to go out throughout all the Worlds. Not a pebble was to be left unturned. And when a sector was determined to be "clean", a magical Loki-Excluder force-field would be erected around it. That way, the feds could narrow and tighten the potential area of search, and not have to keep looking at places they'd already looked at.

Loki, meanwhile, headed for the hills. Too late, he'd realized that he'd finally gone too far and that he could never ever return to Asgard. He couldn't hide out in Jotunheim, either, as sooner or later one of the Jotuns would rat on him for the reward. The few friends he had told him to get lost. He had stashed survival gear and canned food here and there, so he wasn't altogether without resources. He also still had his shape-changing magic.

After changing all of his hidden supplies into small, light packets of trail mix which could be easily shoved into his backpack, Loki made his way to Midgard, to a densely-forested and extremely lightly-populated forest area located in a mountain range called "The Smokies". The few folks who did see him thought that he was a moonshiner, and Loki didn't correct their misconception. Instead, he changed some pond water into white lightning, bottled it in Mason jars, and swapped it to the locals for their silence. The locals, recognizing that they could get the Real Good Stuff that their grandparents had known and loved, were as good as their word. As long as they could keep the "revenooers" away from "Luke", this supply would continue to be available.

"Luke" (as he was known in those parts) set up camp next to a large waterfall. The thunder of the water falling onto the rocks below would drown out any noise he might make, and there was always plenty of water available for him to change into rotgut. He built a low bunker there, disguised to look like natural rock. If you looked closely at it, though, you could see the gun-slits. Loki wasn't going to take any chances.

Meanwhile, back at The Valhalla, huge maps of all the Worlds were tacked to the walls. Areas which had been searched and pronounced "clean" were highlighted in yellow after the force-fields were set. Urd had her crystal ball set up on one table, and Odin sent the ravens and wolves along with the searchers. The Valkyries, Einherjar, and the Hell's Angels covered Muspellheim, Jotunheim, and the seamier sides of the other Worlds. Heimdall activated his "rat line", offering pardons and/or cash rewards to his informants for any news of Loki. Ægir and Ran saw to it that the seas were closed off to Loki, but somehow they didn't check on fresh water ponds, lakes, rivers, creeks, or brooks. Njord's seagulls flew far and wide, checking the coastal and estuarine regions, but they didn't quite get inland far enough to spot Loki's bunker.

It took almost a year before the gods got around to inspecting that anonymous little gorge in which Loki had set up his hideaway. Loki, attuned to the sounds of the waterfall, picked up the sounds of the gods' walkie-talkies and of their combat boots scraping on the rocks as the gods climbed up the gorge from downstream. He slipped out of his bunker, which all of a sudden didn't seem to feel so safe anymore. He leaped into the waterfall, changing himself into a salmon in midair. As a fish, he could logically be there; besides, he wouldn't be the only salmon in that stream.

The gods got up to the waterfall, led by Heimdall's best tracker, Chief Detective Kvasir Holmes. Kvasir spotted the bunker easily, and took photos of the site before approaching the door. He also dusted for fingerprints and did other high-tech detective things. Documentation would be critical for the trial, so Kvasir was taking absolutely no chances. There were no noises inside the bunker and Kvasir's thermal-imaging scope didn't pick up any body-shaped infrared signal from inside, so Hoenir kicked down the door. As he screamed "Go! Go! Go!", Heimdall's SWAT team, guns drawn, poured inside and secured the bunker.

181

Kvasir ordered that all non-police gods stay outside so that the professionals could have a clear field to gather evidence. He did a thorough job of it and amassed a small mountain of tagged evidence bags. When he checked out the still-warm ashes in the fireplace, he suddenly got all intent and focused. He quickly shot four rolls of film (black and white, color, infrared, surveillance) of the scene before disturbing anything. He then sent the film back to the Asgard 1-Hour Photo Lab via the ravens with instructions that the film was to be subjected to computer enhancement and the resulting pictures gotten back to him crash rush.

The pictures came back, confirming Kvasir's deductions. It was time for a serious dragnet, focusing on the waterfall and the stream going to the sea. Loki had been careless, thinking that if he burned the evidence, it would be effectively destroyed. Enough remained, however, so that Kvasir was able to reconstruct exactly what Loki had been up to. Tyr contacted his contractor, Dwarf and Dwarf Military Supplies, for an ultra-strong gill-net, 75 feet long by 12 feet deep. Thor brought it to the bunker, rolled up behind him on his Harley. Ægir, Ran, and Njord "sewed up" the mouth of the stream, and the Einherjar, Hell's Angels, and the Valkyries lined both banks of the stream between the bunker and the sea, weapons at the ready.

The gods strung the net across the stream; Thor holding one end and everyone else the other. They then started walking slowly downstream with their dragnet, alert for their quarry. Loki was still sure that he could outwit the feds, but this net worried him. He tried a "The Fugitive"/"The Pretender" sequence of disguises in hopes of escaping detection. Again and again the net swept down the stream, while the watchers at the bank and the mouth of the stream watched intently for any signs of the suspect. Odin thought at one point that something had caught and then wiggled free from the net.

"He's somewhere in this stream, boys!" Odin announced hoarsely to the rest of the gods and goddesses. "The murderer of my son is *not* going to escape the vengeance of the Law!"

Now, Odin was pretty much The Law in those parts. As town magistrate, he sat in judgement at the Asgard Court House. Mostly he'd had to deal with Drunk & Disorderly or Driving Under the Influence. But this would be a capital case. Mimir would have to be the court-appointed defense counsel since Forseti, Balder's son, had signed up as the prosecutor. Heimdall, Tyr, and Sif were more than ready to testify as prosecution witnesses.

Chief Detective Holmes suggested that they weight the net so that it really *would* scrape the bottom. Thor was all for using grenades, but Odin stopped him just before he pulled the pin of the first one. Fishing with grenades was *so* much fun, suggested the thunder god with a tight grin, and it would serve Loki right. He was always trying to be our chum, why not *let* him? Be chum, that is . . . .

Again the net swept the stream, the lead weights dragging and catching on rocks and snags in the bottom of the streambed. Loki frantically tried to evade it. His choices were three: swim ahead of it to the sea (but there, Ægir and Ran had a school of great white sharks mixed in with a lot of barracuda hopefully waiting for such a move), hop back over the net toward the waterfall (which would buy him some time), or get caught (in which case he'd be toast). Ever the optimist, Loki selected option number 2.

183

A great shout arose from the watchers and fishermen when Loki, in the shape of a salmon, leaped high over the net toward the waterfall. Urd's crystal ball . . . yes, she was on site by now . . . revealed Loki's true shape to all. The sounds of a very large assortment of weaponry being cocked, safeties being released, and rounds being chambered echoed off the walls of the gorge. Thor had his hands full of net, which meant that he couldn't use either the grenades or his hammer. Odin was so angry at this point that his hands shook, and everybody gave him plenty of room.

"Thor! Drop your end of the net! Everybody else on the net, I want two teams, one on either end! Thor, you walk *behind* the net so that if Loki tries to leap over again, you can catch him!"

The thunder god threw Odin a salute, tugged at his biker's gloves and tossed a grenade through the waterfall to make sure that Loki wasn't hiding between it and the rock. He wasn't. The net was strung across the stream and held on both ends by all the Æsir and Vanir (except Idunn and Bragi). And as they started their sweep downstream, Thor waded out into the stream behind the belly of the net, ready for anything.

Well, sometimes the smartest criminal can get a case of the stupids. That's what happened with Loki. He tried to jump the net again. Why he didn't change into an anchovy and swim right through the net escapes me, but he didn't. Maybe he didn't think that being an anchovy was dignified enough. Anyhow, Thor was right there, and he snagged Loki in both hands. The slippery fish tried to wiggle free, but Thor's grip tightened on Loki's body right ahead of the tail. That's how come fish bodies narrow down to almost nothing just before their tails. Didn't know that, did you, children?

Thor waded ashore, careful not to let Loki escape. The feds were there, eagerly waiting with enchanted handcuffs, Mace, billy clubs, leg-irons, duct tape, a cattle prod or two, and one syringe full of sodium pentothol donated by the Asgard Ladies' Ambulance Auxiliary. Sif also had a carving knife which she'd sharpened for just this occasion. Odin neutralized Loki's shape-change spell. He also took away Loki's ability to use magic, leaving Loki helpless, naked, and whining on the rocks. The feds pounced on him and trussed him up like a Thanksgiving turkey. Or like Fenris. Whatever. No way was Loki going to get out of this one.

Odin opened court right there in front of the waterfall. He used a big rock for his judge's desk, and a small rock for a gavel. The evidence was on site, ditto the witnesses. Forseti and Mimir consulted with their respective clients. Loki snarled and growled, but after the sodium pentothol took hold (Mimir objected to its use, overruled by Odin), he quieted down. Forseti started questioning him (again, Mimir objected but was overruled) and the truth started spilling out. Years of petty larceny through Murder One were revealed to all. When the case went to the jury, the verdict was back in less than a minute. Guilty on all charges, including a few . . . and here they are . . . which weren't even in the original docket.

Heimdall, Odin, Tyr, and Thor took great pleasure in tossing Loki into the slammer. It was a rather crude prison, with scorpions and snakes living in the (enchanted) roof. The enchanted bars are impassible, and the door is welded shut on its frame. Loki can only see his sweetie on Visitors' Day. She tries smuggling in thermite as "shoe polish", files in cakes, a hand grenade in a cantaloupe, that sort of thing. But every single thing sent in to Loki is scanned by X-ray before being hand-inspected. Nothing in the way of contraband has yet made it in to Loki's cell.

The snakes above Loki's head drool, and when their poison hits Loki, he pounds the wall in his frantic efforts to escape. Shakes the whole place. But he's got nine life sentences (sequential) with no time off for good behavior, so he's stuck. Sif personally threw away the key. Actually, she had it melted down and cast into a cute little pendant that she wears day and night.

Well, children, that's the story for tonight. I don't think we'll be hearing much more about Loki. He blew it bigtime, and now he's finally having to pay for his life of crime. What's that? No, children, Loki can't just pay a fine. Loki was guilty of a *lot* more than just speeding. Now go to sleep, and in the morning, we can take a nice walk and maybe get in some fishing.

Chapter 17

THE WAR TO END ALL

Well, hullo, there, children! Are you ready for another story? Great! I really wish that this weren't the last one right now, but my vacation is over and I have to go home. I will sure miss telling you your bedtime stories, but come my next vacation, you betcha I'll have a whole pile of new ones for you!

The weather was really rotten in Denmark, as well as in the rest of Midgard. It was nasty and sullen and humid, with frequent storms and cold bursts of hail. This meant that your average Viking was in a crabby mood, which meant that there were more than the usual axe-fights, bar-room brawls, and mayhem in general. The weather wasn't much better in Asgard, either. This meant that pretty much everybody stayed inside. This was no hardship in The Valhalla, where good cheer was as available as the beer on tap. The Einherjar barely noticed the rain or snow or sleet or hail.

Odin sipped at a Snail Trail Pale Ale as he idly flipped through a pamphlet which a traveling salesman from Muspellheim had dropped off at The Valhalla, along with a trial sample of his company's product. "An Axe Time, a Sword Time, a Wind Time, and a Wolf Time . . . ." Odin read. Sounded pretty exciting to him. He read on.

It would all begin with a new ice age, mortal humans running amok, the wolf Skoll eating up the sun and her brother Hati devouring the moon. Blood all over the place. Earthquakes, falling buildings and trees, and a falling doghouse out in back of The Valhalla. That meant that Fenris would be free, and the End of Time would be upon the gods. Loki would probably get sprung, too. Roosters throughout The Worlds would start crowing, to be answered by the sirens on Heimdall's toll booth. Heimdall himself would then come tearing out of the booth, hoping to get out one last Extra! edition of the *Gjallarhorn Gazette* before the power plant blew. Shipwrecks, the dead rising from their graves, and the Midgard Serpent finally getting tired of chewing on his tail. That meant that the Worlds were getting unzipped and that this was going to be The War To End All.

This was awfully worrisome to Odin. He stared at the pamphlet, and then at the gaudily-painted video arcade game which came with it. This booklet spelled out some mighty specific things and named some mighty local names. He checked to see who was the manufacturer. It was no surprise to see that both the booklet and the machine were made by Muspellheim Dreamworks. So they were branching out into video games, thought Odin. Maybe just sending nightmares wasn't enough for them. Well, maybe this would liven things up at The Valhalla. One could only play poker so long.

Flash! A bulletin suddenly came in that the armies of Jotunheim and Muspellheim were mobilizing. Intelligence from Heimdall's agents in place confirmed this, and also that the two armies were intending to attack Asgard and wipe out everyone and everything in it. Odin would have to take immediate action. His mission, and he'd better decide to accept it, would be to save the Worlds.

Odin rocked back on his heels, his expression grim. The Einherjar dropped their cards, drinks, dime novels, whatever, and grabbed their weaponry. It was crunch time, which meant All Hands On Deck. Hod came inside from his usual station by The Valhalla's front door, shivering and dripping wet. He carefully emptied his swizzle stick inventory out of his horn before pouring out a pint of sleety water onto the floor. One of the Valkyries, who was tending the bar, filled Hod's horn with hot buttered rum. Hod cupped his trembling hands around the horn, hoping to warm them as he gratefully sipped the steaming rum.

Thor was the next one who came into The Valhalla. As he opened the door, the gusty hail-laden wind blew his jacket up over his head. He thrashed about wildly to free himself from the sodden leather while another Valkyrie struggled to close the door.

"(A very interesting selection of naughty words)!" growled the thunder god, throwing the wet jacket into one corner of the barroom. "What's a winter hurricane doing coming to Asgard? The way it's blowing, I think we might lose that big ash tree on the town green! And if that tree goes, it'll mash half the town including my gym!"

Thor shook himself like a large dog. Odin's expression and the weaponry in the hands of the Einherjar then caught his attention. His hand whipped down to his belt after Mjollnir. Things looked as if they were just about to go from bad to much, much worse. Sleipnir, the Amazing 8-Legged Horse smashed open his stall door and stumbled into The Valhalla, with Mimir right on his tail. The horse obviously wanted human (or divine, in this case) company, as it was really lonely in his stall and the noise of the storm was scaring him. Mimir was carrying a huge load of ledgers, papers, files, and documents which he'd rescued from the flooding basement of the Vanaheim Memorial Library. He tried to enlist some helpers to save the rest of the endangered paperwork, but everybody was too intent on what Odin was doing.

Time to select weapons. Odin grabbed his antique spear, Gungnir, and hopped onto Sleipnir's back. The magic eddied around them as they clattered back through the kitchens and out the rear door. The cinderblock and concrete doghouse to which Fenris had been chained was a pile of rubble. Odin had barely enough time to swing his long spear around before the maddened Fenris was upon him. Had he chosen a sword or a sawed-off shotgun, Odin would have stood more of a chance. An eight-foot spear can be awfully unwieldy when a vicious wolf/?/Rottweiler was at your throat, trying to rip it out. Odin was out of the game.

The next up was Frey. He faced a huge fire giant, a normally phlegmatic individual named Surt. Frey was armed with only his next movie contract, which didn't help matters as it burned nicely. Had he had his Purdey's shotgun, the one that never missed, he coulda plugged Surt and gone on to the next level of battle. Two down.

Tyr was paired with Hela's bluetick hound. Amazingly, the dog was all a-bristle and teeth. Not like the Garm everybody knew at all. Tyr tried to beat him off with a stick, but Garm got in on Tyr's right side and nailed him. A series of heavy explosions out on Main Street brought folks to the window of The Valhalla. Loki, who'd escaped from jail and who'd somehow found a bazooka, had come gunning for Heimdall, the head Fed. Heimdall had had just enough time to fire his grenade launcher before the bazooka shell hit his badge. Double kill.

Thor bailed out of the door, hammer at the ready. There, slithering improbably up Main Street toward The Valhalla, was Jormungandr, the Midgard Serpent. His insanely-gleaming yellow eyes fixed themselves on Thor. He opened his mouth wide, intending to swallow Thor just as he'd swallowed that bull head Thor'd used for bait to catch him . . . you children remember Thor's fishing trip, don't you? Thor grinned as the storm-winds whipped his hair; this time he'd *land* the sea serpent! He threw Mjollnir at its snout just as Jormungandr opened wider . . . why, the snake's nostrils disappeared into the low-flying clouds and its lower jaw dug a furrow in the pavement as it lunged for the thunder god. Mjollnir smacked back into Thor's hand just as the serpent's mouth closed over him and swallowed. Hard to throw a hammer when you're being swallowed. And a sea serpent's stomach acid can rot out almost anything that isn't a sea serpent stomach.

Meanwhile, in back of The Valhalla, a shoemaker named Vidar grabbed Fenris by the nose, stomped hard on the wolf/?/ Rottweiler's lower jaw, and made a wish. You children know how to make a wish with a chicken wishbone, don't you? Well, that's what happened to Fenris. Heck, Vidar was so mad he ripped the wolf/?/Rottweiler clean in half! One half had the legs, belly, and lower jaw, the other half had the nose, eyes and ears, back, and tail. I guess the shoe was mightier than the spear. Which reminds me; your Mom said she's taking you to the mall tomorrow for some sturdy new school shoes.

The Einherjar had to battle the armies of Jotunheim and Muspellheim. It took awhile, but they were also wiped out to a man. The Valkyries didn't do much better, though they *did* take out Utgard-Loki. Surt, the fire giant who'd gotten Frey, then hosed down the shattered remains of the town with flaming napalm. Magni and Modi, Thor's twin sons, did very well, by contrast. But then, they were young and had quick reflexes; they also played on the local school football team. One tackled Surt high and the other tackled him low. Magni, who had Surt's head, demonstrated a clever usage of The Istanbul Twist on the giant. Modi, at Surt's feet, had to content himself with breaking every bone in the giant's body.

When the storm and shouting were over, there were bodies all over the place. Smoking rubble lined the street, and a charred stump marked where that big ash tree had stood. Slowly a few bedraggled, battered gods staggered out onto Main Street to compare notes and see what they should do next. Hoenir was in good shape; he'd been down in his bomb cellar playing solitaire during the storm. Magni and Modi, Vidar, and Hod (who had finally gotten warm) met Balder (or his hologram) and Hela coming into town. Hela needed all the help she could get; even a death-goddess couldn't even *begin* to cope with that many bodies all at once.

The sun came out as the gods and goddesses who'd survived stood out there on the rubble-strewn waterlogged street. You know how bright the sun is after a hurricane? Sunlight glinted off puddles in the street and turned the torn leaves and branches of the fallen ash tree to gold. Magni found Thor's hammer-head (the shaft was missing) in one puddle where the sea serpent had spat it out. Modi picked up a torn yellow beer coaster emblazoned "The Valhalla" and carefully put it in his pocket. The Worlds would never see such a great watering hole as The Valhalla ever again.

You children look sad . . . what, do you think that that was the end of Asgard? Calm down there, I still have some more of this story to tell you. Hey, stop crying, it isn't the end at all!

Odin looked up from the video arcade game that they all had been trying out. "Ragnarok: The War To End All!" was painted in jagged red runes above the colorful screen, which was cheerfully inviting them to play another game. The storm still howled outside The Valhalla, but inside, it was warm and dry. Hod emptied his horn of hot buttered rum and hopefully held it out for a refill. As the bartender Valkyrie poured Hod another shot, Thor finished drying his hair and face on the curtains. Frey and Skirnir were celebrating the new movie contract with a bottle of imported champagne, and the Einherjar went back to their varied card games, backgammon, sword-sharpening, tall tale-telling, and snooker.

Vidar, the shoemaker, noticed that the storm was abating and that soon the sun would be out. The howling they heard wasn't the storm winds, it was just Fenris out in back, complaining about the hail. Heimdall suggested to Odin that maybe the folks in Asgard weren't ready for video games, and that maybe that salesman from Muspellheim oughta take it back. Odin agreed heartily. He didn't like the scenarios that it played out; Muspellheim always seemed to win.

And so, children, that's why video arcade games are banned from The Valhalla. That coin-operated bucking bull on The Valhalla's veranda was enough in the way of technology for the folks in Asgard. But it seems that the Muspellheim Dreamworks salesman was a lot more successful here in Midgard. Maybe that's how come so many folks think that Ragnarok actually happened and that the old gods are dead.

OK, it's time for you to close your eyes and go to sleep. Tomorrow you can help me pack, and then when I come back here on my next vacation, I will have a whole pile of new stories about Asgard and Thor and all for you. Good night, and sweet dreams!

Chapter 18

THE LAY OF THE LAND

A sgard, your typical dysfunctional gated suburban town, is located on an island which lies on one side of the Ginungagap Gorge. The mainland, including Midgard and Jotunheim, lies on the other. The waters of the Ginungagap are unnavigable even by experienced white-water boatmen, so the only way to get to Asgard from the mainland is via the Bifrost Bridge. One also has to get past Heimdall, who never seems to sleep and who never forgets a face.

Asgard has a town green with a central ash tree, called

Yggdrasil by the locals. The origin of that name is shrouded in mystery, but somehow a moose, a keg, and Freyja seem to be involved. On one side of the green is The Valhalla Sports Bar and Grill, which has a coin-fed bucking bull on its veranda. It also features loud music, drunken parties, all-you-can-eat barbecued pork ribs, neon signs advertising beer, and a devoted crowd of regular customers. There is a wide-screen TV in the lounge so that when the Jotunheim football team is playing, everybody can get a good view and cheer them on. Odin, the proprietor and permittee, is usually there every night, sitting in his personally name-tagged chair. The name on the tag, scrawled in Swedish-Danish "Common" runes, reads *Hlidskialf Manufacturing Company.* Odin doesn't like it at all if anybody else presumes to sit there. On either side of The Valhalla are paved parking lots. On the far side of the parking lots are abandoned buildings. This may well be because the Valhalla is a rather raucous place and open 24 hours a day, 365 days a year except for leap year, when it's open for 366 days.

Up the street a bit is the Thrudheim Athletic Club. Not only is it a gym where one can work out, but it also has a dojo, boxing ring, indoor track, Olympic pool, weightlifting room, and personal trainers. It also hosts the local chapter of Hell's Angels. Thor holds the all-time record in the weight-lifting department and, since he owns the place, the other customers don't really want to challenge Thor's record.

Not far from the gym is Post 912 (Asgard Chapter) of the VFW. Tyr may frequently be found there, polishing the weapons on the wall, loafing at his desk, or polishing his medals. He also recruits for the Marines, Army, Air Force, and NRA from that same desk. He lets Njord handle the Navy, Coast Guard, Merchant Marine, and Whale Watch International.

On the far side of the green, one can find The Golden Apple Health Food Store, run by the ever-cheerful Idunn. If you like New-Age music and organic food, that's the place for you. She holds psychic fairs once a month, and poetry slams twice a year.

The Vanaheim Memorial Library is next door to Idunn's gaily-painted establishment. It's a standard library, although rather heavy on occult, military, self-help, and law books. It is also much, much larger on the inside than its outside appearance suggests.

On the other side of the Golden Apple is the Wierd Sisters Occult Bookshop and Tea Room (Fortunes Told), run by the Norn sisters (Urd, Verdandi and Skuld) who live upstairs. It's a cosy Tudor-style bungalow set back from the road with a neatly-trimmed boxwood hedge in front, pink moss roses and wisteria growing up the sides almost to the thatched roof, and diamond-pane leaded glass windows. Its front door is painted Kelly green, and has a large brightly-polished brass door-knocker shaped like a dragon right in the middle.

The Asgard Opera House, made of Impressive Marble and looking a lot like a courthouse, is situated on the other side of the Vanaheim Memorial Library. Its usual fare tends towards Wagner, Grieg, and obscure works by Scandinavian student composers. The time they staged Gilbert and Sullivan's "Pirates of Penzance" with the pirates done up as Vikings and the maidens as British nuns was a sell-out, though, and Skirnir is seriously planning to cast "Patience" this summer. Word has it that the Grenadiers will be Jomsvikings and the maidens will all be Icelandic skaldic poets . . . .

At the end of the road, a fancy wrought-iron Gothic-style fence surrounds the Hell-Hole Funeral Home. Hela had been on a tour through Disney World once, saw their version of a haunted mansion, and had a copy built. Her version, however, features dragon-head roof ornaments and a souvenir shop in the lobby. Instead of an organ, she has the services of Garm's vocal talents, which are sure to cause distressed expressions and to bring tears to the eyes of the mourners and occasional tourists.

On the far side of the island is the Great Salty Sea, where Njord and his wife Skadi run the "Fresh Fish Here!" stand. Actually, Skadi tries to be as far from the odiferous ambiance of the docks as she can, so poor Njord has to not only supply the fish, but also to scale, gut, and sell them. It's just as good for Njord's peace of mind that he doesn't know that Skadi is shacking up with Ullr. Njord also sells bait, tackle, and hot clam chowder.

About a mile out to sea, Drs. Aegir Hlersson and Ran Jotunsdottir run a state-of-the-art sea-floor oceanographic research station. Their nine daughters, all grad students in marine ecology/biology, wave physics, fishery studies, marine geology, etc. may frequently be found in the vicinity doing field-work towards their degrees. They're very sociable folks, and have a Web Page second only to Hela's. They love to entertain, as it can get kind of lonely out at sea on a research station.

Midgard is the World which we humans live in. Jotunheim, the land of the giants . . . they like to call themselves Jotuns with the "J" pronounced like a "Y" . . . was on the mainland side of the Bifrost Memorial Bridge. Most of the Jotuns are not really giant-sized, except for the football team and Utgard-Loki's bouncers. The gods don't usually go there except for Thor, who likes to use it for target practice. Other Worlds included Muspellheim (a Mordor wanna-be), Niflheim (a foggy, frozen version of Muspellheim), Alfheim (where the elves and fairies . . . including the Tooth Fairy! . . . live and play), Dvergheim (the dwarves like to live underground in sort of a Habitrail series of warrens), and Vanaheim (mostly Frey's extensive farmlands and rental properties, the Folkvang Hotel, and The Fighting Stallions Disco Club).

Chapter 19

DRAMATIS PERSONAE

THE ÆSIR: These are, generally speaking, the upscale "new-money" gods and goddesses who moved into Asgard when the town was just getting to be an attractive suburban investment. Magic and supernatural powers are everyday normal attributes to them, nothing out of the ordinary.

Odin: the 1-eyed John Wayne-like proprietor of The Valhalla Sports Bar and Grill. Sometimes wanders around town in baggy old sweats, a ratty blue cloak, a John Deere baseball cap pulled down low, and an antique 8-foot spear named *Gungnir*. Greying mustache, hair. Was forced to shave his impressive beard (but got to keep his mustache) as a compromise with Frigg, who was tired of getting big mouthfuls of hair whenever he kissed her. He's the mayor (and chief magistrate) of Asgard, with two ravens and two wolves for staff. Not necessarily known for altruism. Can lie like a rug if it suits his political (or other) needs. Definitely has an eye for the ladies and for money-making schemes.

Frigg: Odin's wife, a Martha Stewart wannabee with big hair. Used to her husband's tall stories and those "late nights at work". A patient woman, she also uses her knowledge of those "late nights at work" to blackmail her husband into doing something for her, such as mowing the lawn or washing the dishes. Chairperson of the Asgard Women's Committee, the Homemaker's Club, the Historical Society, and the Volunteer Fire Department Ladies' Auxiliary. Used to taking charge and running things; definitely Mrs. Mayor. Can be somewhat of a snob. Her son, Balder, is her precious darling.

The Valkyries: an all-girl heavy-metal punk-rock band which plays at The Valhalla. When not actually performing, the girls wait on tables and also are employed as bouncers. Odin claims that they're all his daughters, but the old fella has been known to tell a few whoppers in his time.

The Einherjar: A bunch of fellows who aren't actually Æsir, but who hang out almost 24 hours a day at The Valhalla. The "regulars", like on "Cheers". They can cash their Social Security checks at the bar and, since the Asgard Post Office is located behind the bar, they never have to leave the place if they don't want to. These regulars are fiercely proud of their status, since one of their perks is a quart-capacity drinking horn with each man's name engraved on it; when not in use, the horns hang on the Einherjar Members Only Wall.

Thor: Good-hearted honest biker type, not known for intellectual pursuits. Is usually found at the Thrudheim Athletic Club with some of his buddies. Drinks beer by the 6-keg pack, thinks MacDonalds is a gourmet restaurant. Enjoys no-holds-barred fistfights, monster truck rallies, and other similarly refined entertainments. Red-haired/bearded, drives a customized Harley (with goats' horns for handlebars), carries a magical short-handled sledgehammer called *Mjollnir* (Miller Time!) [note: Mjollnir literally means "grinder-into-flour"]. When he gets mad, he gets even. Noisily. Permanently.

Sif: Thor's main squeeze. "Scooter Trash". Natural blonde hair which reaches to her butt, leather jacket type who only has eyes for Thor. Won't admit to any brief flings with Frey. Likes her men hunky, virile, and honest. Has absolutely *no* use for Loki; thinks he should get the electric chair at best.

Tyr: An older fellow, sort of a war veteran. Belongs to the VFW and the NRA, marches every Memorial Day. Lost a hand during a difficult combat mission, proud of his Purple Heart. Has no use for draft-dodgers, liberal Democrats, or anything in the canine family. Buzz-cut (WW II style) full head of steel-grey hair, can still fit his old uniform (which is more than Odin can say . . .)

Heimdall: Toll collector on the Bifrost Bridge leading to Asgard. Can spot an out-of-towner every time. Also is the owner, editor, reporter, staff photographer, and printer for the local newspaper, the *Gjallarhorn Gazette*. Is also in charge of the FBI, the CIA, and Treasury, notably its BATF (Bureau of Alcohol, Tobacco and Firearms) division. Has phenomenal eyesight and an even more phenomenal memory, which is why malefactors hate to see him show up at their trials as a prosecution witness. Especially when he grins at them with his 24-karat gold-plated smile.

Balder: Airhead, totally clueless male model, sort of a blond Fabio lookalike. Frequently featured in Evian, Poland Springs, and Perrier ads. Beefcake, but the innocent type who believes almost anything he's told, obeys his parents, helps little old ladies cross the street and rescues cats from trees. Had been an Eagle Scout. Probably the only male Asgardian who *hasn't* had a roll in the hay with Freyja (to her deep regret . . .). Toothpaste-ad smile, manly cleft chin, and baby-blue eyes, a real Dudley Do-Right type. Almost too good and pure to bear.

Nanna: Balder's wife, a quiet unassuming type who tends to fade into the woodwork. A real homebody, likes quilting and daytime TV.

Forseti: Balder and Nanna's son, the one who went to Yale Law School. He's in politics now, and is aiming for an ambassadorship to the UN. Has done exceptionally well in the stock market and has a mansion which makes Bill Gates' place look like a cottage. Good-looking, tanned yuppie with a designer briefcase, a Lexus, and a trophy wife.

Loki: "Honorary Member of the Æsir" because he'd been officially adopted by Odin during a drunken moment. He's a loose cannon, an unrepentant weisenheimer who thinks that he's smarter than the rest of the gods. Had originally been a juvenile delinquent and elementary-school dropout from Jotunheim and, whenever caught for a crime/practical joke, prank, vandalism, petty or grand larceny, drunk & disorderly, driving without a license . . . the list goes on . . . "he was not there" "it wasn't his fault" "someone else was actually responsible" etc., or he'll quickly and skillfully change the topic of conversation. Unsurpassed at "weasel words" like some folks in D.C. Will do rash impulse things just for kicks like chopping off Sif's hair, without figuring on the fact that Thor would find out about it and beat him to a pulp. Has somehow survived, in spite of having been caught and severely punished by almost every resident of Asgard. Sort of a weedy guy with a pasty complexion (except for the acne), and a whining way of talking.

Hela: Runs the Hell-Hole Funeral Home. Creepy place, a big favorite for Hallowe'en "Haunted House" tours. She looks a bit like Morticia of the Addams Family, which pleases her no end. It has been rumored that Loki was her father, but since she runs a reputable joint, she tends to disavow any such connection.

Idunn: Runs the "Golden Apple Health Food Store" in town. Macrobiotic, vegan, no preservatives-or-artifical-ingredients type, organic farmer/herbalist on the side. Wants to Save the Whales and the Rainforest and Baby Harp Seals. A real flower-child hippie. Bragi's wife.

Bragi: Brewer *par excellence*, supplies The Valhalla with all its alcoholic needs. Great stuff, even though it's been brewed solely from macrobiotic, organically grown, politically correct, environmentally friendly heirloom grain. He is also the organizer of (and main performer at) Idunn's poetry slams.

Hoenir: Even more of an airhead than Balder, but everyone thinks he's so smart because he keeps his trap shut. He's even more closemouthed than Calvin Coolidge, which is going some. Big, beefy guy, looks a lot like Hulk Hogan in his prime. Heavily into survivalist games.

Mimir: Small-time lawyer-*cum*-stock broker, incredibly erudite and learned but very shy and has trouble speaking up in public. This doesn't keep him from being a "talking head" on "Wall $treet Week" and "Nightly Business Report", two of Odin's favorite PBS programs. Almost otherworldly; would rather be deep in the bowels of the Vanaheim Memorial Library than anywhere else. Tags along with Hoenir, a major client, whom he advises.

Hod: Blind homeless slightly retarded drifter who makes a living selling swizzle sticks outside The Valhalla. The Einherjar make sure that he gets plenty of business.

Ægir: Lives in a deep-sea research station with his wife, ***Ran***. His Ph.D. is in oceanography/marine biology, hers is in hotel management. Both consider Njord as somewhat of a landlubber. In his spare time, Aegir brews craft beers ("Sunset Seaweed IPA" and "Davy Jones Lager" are perennial favorites). They have nine daughters, all grad students in some aspects of marine science. Technically they are Jotuns, but they tend to downplay that as most Jotuns barely make it to eighth grade.

The Norns: Nobody's sure whether they're Æsir or Vanir, since they've always been there. Although of three generations, they are sisters and are renowned fortune tellers. Urd, the eldest, specializes in pre-Viking period techniques; Verdandi, the middle sister, in Viking through nineteenth century divination, and young Skuld is a gung-ho New-Ager. They also have a 100% accuracy record.

THE VANIR: These gods and goddesses were the original founders and settlers in Asgard, "old money", salt-of-the-earth. Don't feel that they have to dress in Crag Claybjørn outfits or buy toys from Sharpest Image.

Frey: Well-endowed hunk, fond of posing in dramatic attitudes. Ruggedly handsome in a kind of Harrison Ford way; wants to make it big in Hollywood. In the meantime, he's a grain farmer (barley, wheat, oats) who firmly believes that his crops won't grow unless he goes out and "makes it" in the fields to show the grain what to do. Has the appetites of a 3-ball tomcat in springtime. Also owns a prizewinning pedigreed boar, "Golden Bristles of Vanaheim" whose stud fee easily comes in at $1,500-plus.

Skirnir: Frey's publicist. A fine dramatic actor in his own right, he manages the Asgard Amateur Players and consults with the Asgard Opera Guild. He would do simply *anything* for Frey.

Byggvir: Frey's hired farmhand. Actually runs the place while Frey is out auditioning, performing, or tomcatting around.

Beyla: Byggvir's wife. She helps her husband and oversees getting the grain to market. She also runs the farm stand and takes produce to the weekend Farmer's Market on the town green.

Freyja: Bimbette with singularly loose morals and a creative attitude toward sex. A sucker for love poetry, and is always in love with somebody (or somebodies). Goes in big for clunky costume jewelry (especially necklaces), cats, chocolate, teddies from Victoria's Secret, and whipped cream (either taken internally or applied externally). Fraternal twin of Frey. If she gets mad at someone, it isn't just a hissy fit; she'll throw knives, etc. at that someone's 10-ring.

Njord: Grizzled sea-dog skipper who, when not engaged in Coast Guard/SAR duties, can usually be found either fixing his boat, out fishing in it, or at his dockyard "Fresh Fish Here!" stand. Perennially smells of seaweed, old fish, and Stockholm tar. Looks a lot like the Gortainn Seafood man (yellow slicker, "salty" beard, rolling walk). Best weather forecaster in Asgard. In spite of his weatherbeaten grubby sailor-man looks, he is also one of the wealthiest men in Asgard . . . but even his personal accountant (and certainly the IRS) is ignorant of the full extent of Njord's holdings.

Ullr: Ski bum in the winter, year-round bow-hunter. Has no use for meat that he hasn't hunted down and shot. Has no use for organic vegetables either, except for maybe an apple given him by Idunn now and again. Lives in a tarpaper shack, is a redneck who makes his own hooch, clothes, boots, etc. Not much of a social fellow, prefers to stay out in the woods, on the slopes, or in his shack. Skins of various animals are tacked on the walls (he cures/tans his own leather, too). Takes a bath (on purpose) maybe once a year.

Skadi: Thinks that Ullr is sooo romantic, rustic, and maybe someone whose ways she can change. Prep school, snow-bunny socialite, loves venison *rôti avec champignons* by candlelight. Ullr usually serves his venison fried in bear grease on battered blue speckle-finished tin plates, by the light of a Coleman lantern, with a side order of his version of applejack in pint mason jars. In spite of their social differences, Skadi spends a lot of time in that tarpaper shack, on the slopes, or out in the woods with Ullr.

JOTUNS

Utgard-Loki: A real go-getter and slick operator, he runs 'Utgard-Loki's Pool Hall" which features every type of gambling known to god or man. Massive build, booming laugh, wears his black beard in three braids, and very, very seldom loses a bet. Easily the richest Jotun in Jotunheim.

Skrymir: Utgard-Loki's head bouncer. Shaved head, cauliflower ears, no neck, a few missing teeth, and a frequently-mashed-and-healed nose. He doesn't use Left Guard, thinks soap is for sissies, and thinks a day is wasted unless he beats up a dozen people/gods/jotuns/dwarves/whatever.

Hymir: Charter fishing is his business, his love, and his hobby. He also raises dairy and meat cattle, as fishing is definitely *not* the road to riches.

Thrym: Tried computer dating, but after each first date, the dating service would refund his money and tell him to please try their competitors. Has even worse luck in bars. So homely that a warthog looks great in comparison. Desperate to get married, have a family, and live in a nice white suburban house with a serious metalworking shop out back.

Thjazi: Faded football hero; blames the Æsir for his troubles. Subtle as a cinderblock. He'd blame anybody but himself if things went wrong, even if he was clearly his own worst enemy.

Skadi: Thjazi's only child; she became one of the Æsir by marriage.

Ægir: He and his wife *Ran* disavow any connections with the Jotuns, so look for them in the Æsir section.

Hrungnir: Junkyard owner, likes cheap beer, mean dogs, and fast horses. Longish black greasy hair, a large red nose, and a hulking build. One of the giant-sized Jotuns. Keeps to himself unless there's free beer, a dogfight, or a horse race.

Geirrod: Hrungnir's brother. The smart one who can read one-syllable words. He runs "Geirrod's Back-Door Arena", manages the "Jotunheim Jiant Wressling Federation", and is a professional wrestler and wrestling trainer. Has no sons, so his daughters are following in Pop's footsteps.

Grid: Runs "Grid's Motel and Cat House", catering to all tastes. If you ask nicely, she'll take you out back where she has a small shop with special theme party toys, literature, and videos. Strangely enough, she doesn't seem to own any cats.

Gerd: Spectacularly beautiful professional supermodel; not into the Jotun scene. She loves mink, diamonds, classy men, *good* champagne, and romance. None of what 99% of the Jotun males even come *close* to offering her. Delighted to become member of the "Vanir-by-marriage" set.

Hyndla: Hardbitten attendant at the convenience store next to the Midgard Arena and Convention Center. Loves gossip and Harlequin novels. Bitterly resents anything that takes her away from those two items, which means that she's usually pretty grumpy while at work.

Gilling: Married to *Eleanora Sophia Garbanzo*, who has a *very* closely-knit Family. Their only son, *Suttung*, takes after his maternal side. Heimdall has their names, fingerprints, and photos red-flagged.

MORTAL HUMANS:

Geirr Lukas and *Staffan Spelbjerg* are close friends, and often help with each other's movies. World-class directors with very creative approaches to cinematography. They take turns cleaning up in the Academy Awards, and are *very* popular in all the Worlds.

Ole and *Lena Ingqvist* have one teenaged son, *Thjalfi* and one teenaged daughter, *Roskva*. They're big into Skandinavisk-Midgard Association activities, kitch art, and hospitality. Ole and Lena have also been featured in any number of humorous jokes and tales, a few of which are true.

DWARVES:

Fjalar and *Galar* (no last name that they'll admit to) make and sell a singularly potent moonshine which tastes as if it had been stored in an inner tube in the hot sun for a week before being siphoned off. It has a kick like a mule, with a vinyl/vulcanized rubber nose, copper-penny overtones, and slight skunk and mildew notes.

ANIMALS, MONSTERS, AND OTHER BEINGS

Jormungandr: Also called the "Midgard Serpent". Nobody besides Thor has actually seen him and lived, but he figures prominently in most fishermen's tall tale repertoires, generally as "the one that got away".

Fenris: Inbred male junkyard Rottweiler/?/wolf cross with a definite attitude problem. Permanently chained to a cinderblock and cement doghouse in back of The Valhalla Sports Bar and Grill. Sometimes the Einherjar amuse themselves by chucking empties at him. Needless to say, the residents of Asgard hope and pray that he'll never get loose.

Hugin and Munin: Odin's ravens, spies in bird suits. Frigg gets annoyed with them because when they're not out flying around, they like to sit on Odin's shoulders and drop guano down the back of his shirt.

Geri and Freki: Odin's two purebred grey wolves. Unlike Fenris, these are well-mannered and don't need to be chained up. Used to wandering all over town, mostly hoping for kitchen scraps.

Garm: Hela's half-breed bluetick hound, given to howling like a banshee especially during the more solemn bits of a funeral service. Not much good for anything else.

556-SIBL

Sleipnir: Odin's 8-legged grey stallion, abandoned as a foal at The Valhalla by Loki, who was on the run as usual. Any horse with 8 legs would get tangled up even walking, let alone running. Loki claims that he "just found" Sleipnir as a stray colt wandering around in a field. Nobody really believes that story. Sleipnir's *real* origin is one of Loki's deepest-held secrets. The stallion is a featured sideshow attraction at The Valhalla Sports Bar and Grill, as yet another way for Odin to rake in more money.